Go Beyond intro
WORKBOOK

Andy Harvey

Macmillan Education
4 Crinan Street
London N1 9XW
A division of Macmillan Publishers Limited

Companies and representatives throughout the world

ISBN 978-0-230-47808-4

Text, design and illustration © Macmillan Publishers Limited 2016
Written by Andy Harvey

The author has asserted his rights to be identified as the author of this work
in accordance with the Copyright, Designs and Patents Act 1988.

Go Beyond is a registered trademark, property of Macmillan Publishers
International Limited

First published 2016
First edition entitled *Beyond* published 2015

All rights reserved. No part of this publication may be reproduced, stored in
a retrieval system, or transmitted in any form or by any means, electronic,
mechanical, photocopying, recording, or otherwise, without the prior
written permission of the publishers.

Designed by EMC Design Ltd.

Illustrated by Peter Cornwell pp. 33, 34, 36, 49, 68; Venitia Dean
(Advocate-Art) p. 21; Tony Forbes (Sylvie Poggio Artists) p. 14; Kev
Hopgood pp. 23, 25, 50, 79, 94; Jamie Pogue (Bright Agency) p. 4;
Tony Wilkins pp. 23 (boy with glasses, young boy, woman with collared
shirt, woman with bangs), 61, 72 (salad and rice)

Cover design by EMC Design Ltd.
Cover photograph by Alamy/Age Fotostock/Dennis MacDonald
Picture research by Lorraine Beck and Emily Taylor

The author and publishers would like to thank the following for permission
to reproduce their images:

Alamy/Arco Images p. 69(3), Alamy/George S de Blonsky p. 45(t), Alamy/
Robert Crum p. 55(cr), Alamy/Huntstock p. 50, Alamy/Mint Images
Limited p. 44 (br), Alamy/Forget Patrick/Sagaphoto p. 38, Alamy/Radharc
Images p. 46(5), Alamy/Robert Harding World Imagery p. 19(br), Alamy/
Andres Rodriguez p. 59(br), Alamy/YAY Media AS p. 52(tr), Alamy/Zixia
p. 46(4);
Bananastock pp. 16(a tl), 25(c, d), 30(a, f), 95(tr), BananaStock/Punchstock
p. 25(a);
Brand X pp. 4(e, g), 18(4), 20(1.5), 26(1), 60, 97(d), 98(map);
Comstock Images pp. 30(ice cream), 48(tr, bm), 73(a);
Corbis pp. 12(tl), 16(a br), 17, 20(1.9), 30(d, eye), 34(tr), 61(cl),
71(Greenland), 83(4), 103, Corbis/Aflo pp. 47(bl), 52(b), 85(5), Corbis/
Johnér Images/Susanne Kronholm p. 29, Corbis/Isaac Lane Koval
p. 100(tr), Corbis/Monkey Business Images p. 4(bm), Corbis/Ocean/68
p. 98(tr), Corbis/PhotoAlto/Odilon Dimier p. 7(bl), Corbis/SuperStock/
DreamPictures/Shannon Faulk p. 7(br), Corbis/Zero Creatives/Image
Source p. 101;
DigitalStock p. 13(lion), DigitalStock/Corbis pp. 52(cr), 88(br);
Digital Vision pp. 4(d), 46(8), 66, DigitalVision/PunchStock/Studio442
pp. 64(b), 97(c);
Eyewire p. 85(9);
Getty Images pp. 4(a, c), 16(d), 19(tr), 26(5), 30(pen), 39(1, 3), p. 47(br),
59(3), 71(pool), 73(d), 85(1, 8, 10), 91, 95(b), 97(a), Getty Images/Altrendo
Images p. 11(tcm), Getty Images/AWL Images p. 31(tr), Getty Images/
Mark Bowden p. 41, Getty Images/Brand X Pictures/Blend Images p. 85(6,
7), Getty Images/Cultura pp. 15, 96(tr), Getty Images/Werner Dieterich
p. 35(a), Getty Images/EyeWire p32(fish), Getty Images/Fuse p. 84(f), Getty
Images/Hero Images p. 27(br), Getty Images/Jack Hollingsworth p. 86(br),
Getty Images/Maskot p. 99(bl), Getty Images/Image Source/Steve Prezant
p. 22, Getty Images/Tetra Images p. 82(bl), Getty Images/The Image Bank/
Richard H Smith p. 45(b), Getty Images/The Palmer p. 48(br), Getty
Images/Westend 61 p. 99(br);
Image Source pp. 9(tr), 11(bcm, tr), 13(Italy), 20(1.1), 20(1.8), 25(e), 27(cr),
37(cr), 39(6), 46(3), 55(tr), 58, 61(bcr), 62(1, 4, 5), 67(tr), 69(4), 79(b), 84(c),
97(background), 97(b);
Imagestate p. 62(2, 3);
Jupiter Images p. 16(b);
The Kobal Collection/Dreamworks Animation p. 24(2), The Kobal
Collection/Dreamworks/Paramount p. 24(1, br), The Kobal Collection/
Marvel/Sony Pictures p. 24(3), The Kobal Collection/New Line Cinema

p. 24(4, 5), The Kobal Collection/Walt Disney Pictures p. 28(3a),
The Kobal Collection/Warner Bros p. 28(3c), The Kobal Collection/
Warner Bros/DC Comics p. 28(3b);
Macmillan Publishers Limited pp. 16(c, f), 18(1), 26(2), 26(4),
48(bl), 44(1–8), 61(br), Macmillan Publishers Limited/Macmillan
Australia pp. 20(1.11), 30(bike), 72(pasta, chicken), 80(b), Macmillan
Publishers Limited/Macmillan Mexico pp. 8 (glasses, T-shirt, bikes),
23(6.1, 6.2), 42(b), 43(br), 68(bl), 72(pizza, eggs, cheese, steak), 78(a,
b, c, e, f), 80(a, c, d, e, f, g, h, i), 93(soccer ball, guitar, fish), 102(a–f),
Macmillan Publishers Limited/Macmillan New Zealand pp. 18(7),
20(1.3), 78(d), 93(books), Macmillan Publishers Limited/Macmillan
South Africa pp. 8 (ice cream, jeans), 42(t), 72(bread);
Pathfinder p. 18(6);
Photoalto p. 35(g);
Photodisc pp. 4(f), 32(a, chicken, cats, dogs), 39(2), 71(crocodile),
76(tr), Photodisc/Getty Images pp. 13(pizza, br), 16(a, tr), 20(1.4),
20(1.10), 26(6), 30(tiger), 32(b, c, d), 46(6), 67(br), 71(desert), 73(e, f,
globes), 80(sun, mountains), 85(4), 97(tr), PhotoDisc/Getty Images/
Linda Bronson p. 70, PhotoDisc/Getty Images/Cartesia p. 92,
Photodisc/Getty Images/Joshua Ets-Hokin p. 67(cr), Photodisc/Getty
Images/Anthony Saint James p. 76(br);
Photospin p. 86(tr);
Pixtal pp. 25(f), 35(b–e, h);
Purestock/Punchstock/Getty Images pp. 18(2), 80(sky dive);
Stockbyte pp. 5(tr), 30(c), 32(horse), 43(tr), 75;
Stuart Cox p. 84(d);
Studio 8 p. 30(ear);
Superstock p. 88(cr);
Thinkstock pp. 4(b, h), 11(b), 13(car), 12(tcl, bcl), 16(a, bl, e),
18(5), 20(1.2), 20(1.7), 26(3), 27(tr), 30(b, e, panda), 32(e, f, g, mice),
39(4), 43(cr), 46(1), 54, 59(1, 4), 61(cr), 73(b, c), 81(tr), 88(tr),
Thinkstock/BananaStock p. 23, Thinkstock/Dmitriy Burlakov
p. 100(br), Thinkstock/Getty Images pp. 10, 28(br), 30(street), 37(bl),
Thinkstock/Getty Images/BananaStock p. 83(1, 2), Thinkstock/
Getty Images/Fuse pp. 20(6.3), 82(br), 84(e), 85(3), Thinkstock/
Getty Images/iStockphoto pp. 9(br), 12(bl), 13(noodles), 14, 16(tr),
18(3), 18(8), 19(cr), 20(1.6), 20(6.1), 25(b), 28(bl), 30(g, h), 31(cl,
br, cr), 32 (tr), 35(f), 39(5), 40, 48(cr), 59(2), 61(bl), 64(cr), 69(1, 2,
a, b, c), 74, 78(tr), 83(3), 84(b), 85(2), 90, 98(br), Thinkstock/Getty
Images/Purestock p. 28(cl), Thinkstock/iStockphoto/Claudio Arnese
p71(white car), Thinkstock/iStockphoto/Kalulu p. 47(tr), Thinkstock/
iStockphoto/Anzor Mizaushev p. 71(red car), Thinkstock/
iStockphoto/PhilStev p. 46(2), Thinkstock/Jupiter Images pp. 5(bl),
20(6.2), 20(6.5), 84(a), Thinkstock/Medioimages/Photodisc p. 20(6.6),
Thinkstock/Monkey Business Images p. 83(5), Thinkstock/Photodisc
p. 7(tr), Thinkstock/Photodisc/Michael Blann p. 96(b), Thinkstock/
Siri Stafford p. 20(6.4).

These materials may contain links for third party websites. We have
no control over, and are not responsible for, the contents of such third
party websites. Please use care when accessing them.

Printed and bound in China

2020 2019 2018
10 9 8 7 6 5 4

CONTENTS

Starter Get Ready: It's my party — pages 4–7

Unit 1 Me — pages 8–17

Review Unit 1 — pages 18–19

Unit 2 People — pages 20–29

Review Units 1–2 — pages 30–31

Unit 3 Animal magic — pages 32–41

Review Units 1–3 — pages 42–43

Unit 4 Play — pages 44–53

Review Units 1–4 — pages 54–55

Unit 5 Other worlds — pages 56–65

Review Units 1–5 — pages 66–67

Unit 6 Vacation home — pages 68–77

Review Units 1–6 — pages 78–79

Unit 7 Theater workshop — pages 80–89

Review Units 1–7 — pages 90–91

Unit 8 Weather report — pages 92–101

Review Units 1–8 — pages 102–103

GET READY: IT'S MY PARTY
VOCABULARY 1 >>> Numbers 1–20, introductions, colors

1 Match the colors to the things.

1 black ....
2 blue ....
3 brown   *a*
4 green ....
5 orange ....
6 yellow ....
7 red ....
8 white ....

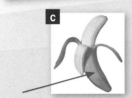

2 Write two more colors.

1 p .... e (= red + blue)
2 p .... k (= white + red)

3 Write the numbers.

a *one*
b ....
c ....
d ....
e ....
f ....
g ....
h ....
i ....
j ....
k ....

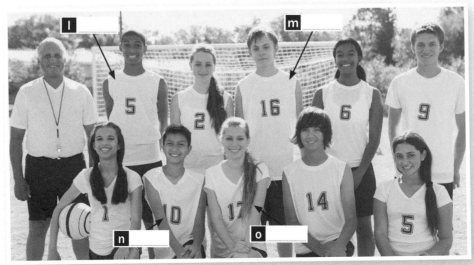

l ....
m ....
n ....
o ....

GRAMMAR 1 Pronouns; Possessive adjectives; *Be*

>>> Hello!

1 Choose the correct option.
1. I like **her** / she.
2. She's **my** / **I** friend.
3. What's **you** / **your** name?
4. Where's **they** / **their** house?
5. **They** / **Their** live on Hill Street.
6. **We** / **Our** dog's name is Ben.
7. That's **his** / **he** name.

2 Complete the text with *I*, *my*, *she*, *her*, *we*, or *our*.

Hi! (1) _My_ name is Leonarda. (2) _____ 'm Mexican. (3) _____ name means "strong as a lion." (4) _____ best friend's name is Esperanza. (5) _____ 's Colombian. (6) _____ name means "hope." (7) _____ 's a very good friend. (8) _____ are together all the time. (9) _____ eat lunch together. (10) _____ favorite activity is dancing.

3 Complete the conversation with *it's* (= it is) or *its*.

Ken: That's our house. (1) _It's_ 8 Lincoln Street.
Jim: It's nice. I like the color.
Ken: Thanks. And this is our old car. (2) _____ name is Daisy.
Jim: Is that really (3) _____ name?
Ken: Yes. (4) _____ a car with (5) _____ own name.
Jim: I like that!

4 Choose the correct option, a, b, or c.
1. That's John. It's ___ birthday today.
   a your   **b** his   c he
2. Mary's in blue. ___ there with Molly.
   a She's   b Her   c Its
3. Mia and Lily are here. ___ clothes are great.
   a Her   b My   c Their
4. Music is great. ___ favorite music is pop.
   a Our   b They   c We
5. I love parties. ___ really fun.
   a They're   b Their   c Your
6. Hi, Brian! ___ here!
   a You   b He   c You're
7. I like the name Lola. Is that really ___ name?
   a you   b my   c your
8. Look at all the food! ___ time to eat.
   a Its   b It's   c It

5 Complete the conversation with *am*, *is*, or *are*.

Leo: Mike (1) _is_ here. We (2) _____ ready to go.
Jack: Wait! Polly and Lucy (3) _____ in the yard. Lucy (4) _____ on her phone.
Leo: Polly! Lucy! Hurry! It (5) _____ late. Let's go!
Lucy: Sorry, guys! I (6) _____ ready now. Let's go.

VOCABULARY 2

>>> Numbers 20–100, days of the week, months; phone contacts

1 a Write the month(s) that …

1	begin with the letter *A*.	Number of days
2	begin with the letter *J*.	
3	begin with the letter *M*.	
4	end with the letters *ber*.	
	September	30
5	begins with the letter *F*.	

b Now write the number of days in each month.

2 Write the days of the week on the calendar.

Friday   Monday   Saturday   ~~Sunday~~   Thursday
Tuesday   Wednesday

3 a 🔊01 Listen and circle the number you hear.
1 (18)   8
2 12   20
3 3   30
4 4   40
5 19   9
6 17   7
7 6   60
8 5   15

b Write all the numbers from Exercise 3a.
1 *eighteen*   *eight*
2
3
4
5
6
7
8

4 Write the numbers.
1 thirty-five   35
2 twenty-one
3 fifty-six
4 eighty-three
5 ninety-seven
6 seventy-four
7 forty-nine
8 sixty-two

5 Look at the Contact Information form. Match the answers (a–e) to the information (1–5).

Contact Information

1 Name:
2 Phone number:
3 Age:
4 Birthday:
5 Address:

a 555-062-8397
b 13
c 20 Sun Street, Miami, USA
d Lucas Johnson
e December 23

OCTOBER

18 Sunday   19_____   20_____   21_____   22_____   23_____   24_____

GRAMMAR 2 *Be*: negative, questions, and short answers; question words

>>> **At the party**

1 a Put the words in order to make questions about a phone.
1 color / it? / is / What — *What color is it?*
2 old / How / it? / is _____
3 it / is / now? / Where _____
4 it / new / Is / phone? / a _____
5 good? / Is / it _____

b Match the questions (1–5) in Exercise 1a to the answers (a–e).
a It's in my bag. ____
b It's black. __1__
c No, it isn't. ____
d It's three years old. ____
e Yes, it is. ____

2 a Complete the questions with *Am*, *Is*, or *Are*.
1 __Are__ you Ella's brother?
2 _____ she your sister?
3 _____ they your friends?
4 _____ I OK?
5 _____ he a gladiator?
6 _____ we ready?
7 _____ it Friday today?

b Match the questions (1–7) in Exercise 2 to the answers (a–g).
a Yes, I am. __1__
b Yes, you are. ____
c No, we aren't. ____
d Yes, it is. ____
e No, she isn't. ____
f Yes, they are. ____
g Yes, he is. ____

3 Write questions and short answers.

1 you / Carol? *Are you Carol?* — ✓ *Yes, I am.*
2 he / your teacher? _____ — ✗ _____
3 we / all here? _____ — ✓ _____
4 they / good friends? _____ — ✗ _____
5 you / in the same class? _____ — ✗ _____
6 it / a good party? _____ — ✓ _____
7 she / OK? _____ — ✓ _____
8 I / on your team? _____ — ✗ _____

4 a Complete the questions with the words in the box.

| How   What (x2)   When   Where (x2)   ~~Who~~ |

1 __Who__ are you?
2 _____ are you from?
3 _____ is your last name?
4 _____ is your birthday?
5 _____ old are you?
6 _____ is your house?
7 _____ is your favorite color?

1 __1__ a I'm Maria.
2 ____ b I'm 13.
3 ____ c It's downtown.
4 ____ d I'm from Venezuela.
5 ____ e It's in December.
6 ____ f It's Gonzalez.
7 ____ g It's yellow.

b Now match the questions (1–7) to the answers (a–g).

UNIT 1 ME
VOCABULARY 1 >>> Things

1 Write the words for the things in the pictures.

1 _phone_   2 _____   3 _____   4 _____

5 _____   6 _____   7 _____   8 _____

2 Write the words (1–7). Then find them in the word search.

1 N O T E B O O K   You write in this.
2 J _ _ _ S   They are clothes.
3 I _ E C _ _ _ M   It is cold and delicious.
4 P _ _ _ E   You talk to people with this.
5 S _ _ _ W _ _ H   It is good to eat.
6 W _ _ S _ _ _   It's on the internet.
7 C _ R   It's a type of transportation. It has a motor.

X	I	C	E	O	W	O	R	G	W
P	S	A	N	D	W	I	C	H	E
H	N	E	C	X	E	O	S	O	B
O	J	E	A	N	S	T	R	V	S
N	E	L	R	B	U	K	E	P	I
E	Q	R	E	Y	T	I	E	N	T
I	C	E	C	R	E	A	M	E	E
N	O	T	E	B	O	O	K	I	D

3 Choose the correct options.

Alex: I like your (1) *sandwich /* **T-shirt**, Angie. Is that a picture of a

(2) *soccer ball / orange* on it?

Angie: Thanks. Yes, it is. And I like your

 (3) *jeans / T-shirt* .

Alex: Thank you, Angie. Let's get a(n)

(4) *ice-cream cone / backpack* . OK?

Angie: Great! Let's go on our

(5) *phones / bikes* .

4 Match the categories (a–f) to the words (1–6).

1 basketball   _e_   a school
2 laptop   _____   b food
3 homework   _____   c clothes
4 sandwich   _____   d technology
5 bike   _____   e games
6 shirt   _____   f transportation

8

READING

>>> **Read an article from a book**

1 **Match the things (a–h) to the verbs (1–8).**

1 eat _g_
2 watch
3 drink
4 use

5 take
6 listen to
7 go to
8 check

a a movie
b coffee
c a taxi
d the internet

e the radio
f a café
g a pizza
h emails

2 **Complete the ad with the words in the box.**

bus café email ~~hotel~~ pizza television

A fantastic (1) _hotel_ on the beach!
• Central location.
• Take the metro, (2) _____ , or taxi from the airport – just 30 minutes.
• Free internet. Check your (3) _____ . Wi-Fi in your room.
• Watch (4) _____ . Sports 24/7.
• Eat in the (5) _____ . Delicious (6) _____ and salad.
• Visit museums – just 10 minutes from the hotel.

3 **Complete the table with words from Exercise 2.**

Transportation	Food	Places
m	p	h_otel_
b	s	m
t		c

4 **What other words in the text (not the names of cities or people) are international words or similar in your language?** _____

MOVE BEYOND

Find an internet site in English about a city in your country. Write six words that are similar to words in your language. Then share them in your next English class.

1 _____ 4 _____
2 _____ 5 _____
3 _____ 6 _____

5 **Complete the article about Miami with the words in the box.**

aquarium café movies museum park room taxi television ~~transportation~~ Wi-Fi

MY WEEKEND IN MIAMI

Saturday:
It's 11:30 a.m. We take public (1) _transportation_ (the Metrorail) to downtown Miami. Then we take a (2) _____ to our hotel. The driver is very nice. We go to a (3) _____ in Miami Beach, and we eat a delicious sandwich. Then we visit the Science (4) _____ . It's very interesting.

Sunday:
We go to the (5) _____ . We see dolphins and whales. Wow! Cool!

Monday morning:
We stay at the hotel in the morning. Our (6) _____ is perfect! We have a (7) _____ with a lot of channels. We have free (8) _____ too. We can surf the internet.

Monday afternoon:
The hotel has a big (9) _____ with pretty flowers and trees. We go there and play soccer. The hotel has a swimming pool, sauna, and gym. It has a movie theater too. Cool! I can watch (10) _____ there.

9

GRAMMAR 1 Plural nouns; a/an, the

>>> Talk about one or more things

1 a Complete the grammar table with the plural nouns.

Singular	Plural
name	names
bus	
class	
lunch	
box	
city	
day	

b Check (✓) the nouns that are always plural.
1. clothes ✓
2. balls ☐
3. jeans ☐
4. sandwiches ☐
5. sunglasses ☐

2) Choose the correct options.

Jessie: I'm (1) **a** / **an** Canadian.

Sandy: I'm (2) **an** / **a** American.

Jessie: I have (3) **an** / **a** ice-cream cone.

Sandy: I have (4) **a** / **an** chocolate cone.

Jessie: And I have (5) **a** / **an** vanilla cone.

Jessie and Sandy: We like ice cream on (6) **a** / **an** hot day.

3) Complete the sentences with *the* or –.
1. I like ___–___ video games. My favorite game is *Wii Sports*.
2. I don't like _____ zoos. Safari parks are better.
3. I take _____ bus to school every morning.
4. I have _____ two dogs. One is named Gimli; the other is Nina.
5. I want _____ black jeans over there. How much are they?
6. I don't want _____ party to end. This is a lot of fun!

4) Choose the best option, a, b, or c.
1. My favorite kind of ice cream is _____ chocolate ice cream.
   a – b the c a
2. I play _____ basketball at school every day.
   a a b – c the
3. I have _____ exam on Monday. Oh, no!
   a – b a c an
4. When is _____ soccer game?
   a a b – c the
5. Excuse me. Where's _____ train station, please?
   a a b – c the
6. Brrr! It's cold. I need _____ cup of hot chocolate.
   a the b a c an
7. I'm on vacation on _____ island in Chile. It's wonderful here!
   a – b an c a

Jessie

Sandy

5 ›› **Complete the text with the plurals of the words in parentheses.**

I have private English (1) _lessons_ (lesson) on Saturdays. I take two (2) _____ (bus) to go to my teacher's house. She lives in a small town because she doesn't like big (3) _____ (city). She's one of my favorite (4) _____ (person). We play language (5) _____ (game), and it's great. My English (6) _____ (class) at school are fun too.

6 ›› **Choose the correct options.**

Tara: How many (1) **childs** / **children** are there in your family?

Jon: There's me and three (2) **babys** / **babies**. They're (3) **girls** / **girles** – my little sisters. They're all ten (4) **months** / **monthes** old.

Adam: Are (5) **men** / **mans** very different from (6) **women** / **womens**?

Una: Yes and no! We're all different (7) **people** / **peoples**.

7 Complete the sentences with *a*, *an*, or (-).

1. **A:** What is in your lunch?
   B: __A__ sandwich and __-__ oranges.
2. **A:** What is in your room?
   B: _____ game console and _____ posters of my favorite team.
3. **A:** His clothes are nice.
   B: He has _____ new jeans and _____ shirt.
4. **A:** What's in your backpack?
   B: _____ English book, _____ notebooks, and _____ phone.

LISTENING

>>> Listen to a description of where things are from

1 Where are these things from – Brazil, Germany, Italy, or Japan? Guess.

1 coffee ....

2 cars ....

3 computers ....

4 clothes ....

LISTENING TIP

Before you listen, think: "What do I know about this topic?" Use your answer to help you understand.

2 ▶02 Listen and check your answers to Exercise 1.

3 ▶02 Listen again and complete the table with the words in the box.

bananas   cars (x2)   clothes (x2)   coffee
computers   famous dances   laptops
risotto   ~~sports cars~~

Italy	Brazil	Germany	Japan
sports cars			

4 Complete the sentences.

1 Italy is famous for its food. I *talian* food is some of the best in the world.
2 Soccer is very popular in Brazil. The B.................... soccer team is very good.
3 Adidas is a G.................... clothing company. Germany has a lot of big companies like Adidas.
4 Japan is famous for sushi. There are J.................... sushi restaurants all over the world.

5 ▶03 Listen to the conversation. Complete the sentences.

1 Avra was on vacation in *Turkey*.
2 The words on Avra's T-shirt are in ....
3 The T-shirt was made in ....

 MADE IN CHINA

6 Complete the table.

Country	Nationality
Turkey	(1) *Turkish*
(2)	English
China	(3) ....

7 ▶03 Listen again and put the words in order.

1 Where's / from? / it
   Where's it from?
2 label? / What's / the / on
   ....
3 know. / don't / I
   ....
4 says / It / "made in China."
   ....

12

VOCABULARY 2

>>> Countries and nationalities

1 Write the country.

1 B r a z i l   2 G_____y   3 I_____y   4 J____n

5 S_____ A_____   6 T_____y   7 U____ed St____s

2 Complete the words in the sentences.
1 Pizza is a famous I*talian* food.
2 S____t A_____ national parks are famous for animals like lions and giraffes.
3 The T_____h city of Istanbul is very old.
4 Porsche is a famous G_____ car company.
5 Taylor Swift is an A_____n singer.
6 People all over the world watch J_____e anime like *Pokémon*.

3 Choose the correct option.
1 *Brazilian* / (*Brazil*) is a very big country.
2 People like to go on a safari in *South Africa* / *South African* .
3 *Italy* / *Italian* is famous for its history.
4 Udon is a *Japanese* / *Japan* food.
5 My English teacher is from Los Angeles. She's *America* / *American* .
6 The *Germany* / *Germans* make very safe cars.
7 I have a *Turkish* / *Turkey* friend.

WORDS & BEYOND

4 a Match the words (a–f) to their opposites (1–6).

1 similar	d	a noisy
2 big		b terrible
3 quiet		c small
4 old		d different
5 great		e boring
6 interesting		f new

b Complete the sentences using words from Exercise 4a.
1 I think math is *boring* . I don't like it.
2 My English class is _____ . Our teacher's great.
3 I love my _____ phone. It's two days old.
4 My sister and I are very _____ people. She's quiet, and I'm noisy!
5 Elephants are very _____ animals.
6 Rome is a very _____ city.

5 Read the clues and write the words. Use the words in the box.

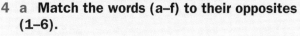

article city game ~~glass~~ sandwich story

1 You use this to drink.   *glass*
2 You eat this.   _____
3 You tell this.   _____
4 You read this.   _____
5 You live in this.   _____
6 You watch this on TV.   _____

6 Complete the words in the text.

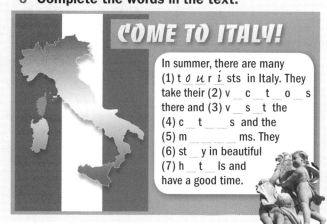

COME TO ITALY!

In summer, there are many
(1) t o u r i sts in Italy. They
take their (2) v__ c__ t__ o__ s
there and (3) v__ s__ t the
(4) c__ t__ s and the
(5) m_____ms. They
(6) st__ y in beautiful
(7) h__ t__ ls and
have a good time.

13

GRAMMAR 2 *This/that, these/those*

>>> **Talk about the things around you**

1 Complete the grammar table with the words in the box.

that   these   ~~this~~   those

Use *this* and *these* to talk about objects near you. Use *that* and *those* for objects far from you.

	Here	There
Singular	What's (1) _this_ ?	What's (2) _____ ?
Plural	What are (3) _____ ?	What are (4) _____ ?

2) Complete the sentences with *is*, *'s*, or *are*.

Cara: What (1) _'s_ this fruit?
Tod: That (2) _____ a mango. It's delicious.
Cara: And (3) _____ those things over there bananas?
Tod: Yes. Those (4) _____ small green bananas.
Cara: (5) _____ those watermelons?
Tod: Yes, those (6) _____ watermelons. They're delicious too!

3 >> Choose the correct options.

Demi: What's (1) *that* / *those* song?
Amy: It's by my favorite group – No Direction. (2) *Those* / *That* boys are great!
Demi: Is (3) *that* / *those* the group from Z-Factor?
Amy: Yes … look: (4) *This* / *These* is their new album.
Demi: I love (5) *that* / *these* pictures of them.

4 a >> Complete the questions with *this*, *that*, *these*, or *those*.

1 Is _this_ my glass here?
2 Are _____ your sunglasses there?
3 Who are _____ people over there?
4 What's _____ picture there on your T-shirt?
5 Is _____ you there in the picture?
6 What's in _____ food here?
7 Are _____ things there real or not?
8 What are _____ things here?

b >> Match the questions (1–8) in Exercise 4a to the answers (a–h).

a No, they're not. _2_
b I think these are green bananas. _____
c They look real to me. _____
d It's Japanese art. _____
e Yes, it's yours. _____
f I don't know. But it looks great. _____
g Yes. I don't look very happy! _____
h They're my teachers. _____

5 >>> Put the words in order to make questions.

1 is / that? / Who
  Who is that?
2 those / What / things? / are

3 Why / this / is / movie / so boring?

4 are / called? / these / What / things

5 this place / Where's / on the map?

6 that / How old / house? / is

14

SPEAKING

Describe things

1 a **Complete the *Phrasebook* with the words in the box.**

are is it It's like really They

b ▶04 **Now listen and check.**

2 ▶05 **Listen to three conversations and answer the questions.**

Conversation 1
1 What country is Lara from? _Brazil_
2 What country is Diego from? _____
Conversation 2
3 Where is Zac? At a _____ .
Conversation 3
4 What color is the girl's room? _____

3 ▶05 **Listen again and match the adjectives (a–f) to the nouns (1–6).**

1 Bogota   _e_
2 Rio   ___
3 party   ___
4 music   ___
5 house   ___
6 room   ___

a small
b noisy
c Brazilian
d new
e capital
f big

4 ▶06 **Listen and repeat these five questions from the conversations. Pay special attention to stress and intonation.**

1 Where are you from, Diego?
2 Is this Brazilian music?
3 What's your house like?
4 What's your room like?
5 What color is it?

5 **Read the example and write a similar conversation.**

Eric: What is your room like?
Ana: It's not big. It's very quiet.
Eric: What's in your room?
Ana: My new laptop. And big posters of my favorite band.

A: (Ask about a backpack.)
_____

B: (Describe the color.)
_____

A: (Ask what is in the backpack.)
_____

B: (Describe things in the backpack.)
_____

PHRASEBOOK

Ask for a description of something
What color (1) _is_ it?
What's your house (2) _____ ?
Is (3) _____ big / small?

Describe something
(4) _____ black / red.
(5) _____ are Italian / Brazilian.
They're very / (6) _____ nice.
The neighbors (7) _____ noisy / quiet.

15

WRITING

>>> Write a description of a thing

1 Complete the tips with the words in the box.

REMEMBER HOW TO …

write a description of a thing

adjective (x2)   noun

- am/are/is + (1) _adjective_ : He's old.
- adjective + (2) _____ : These are my favorite jeans.
- really/very + (3) _____ : That's really nice.

2 Choose the correct option.

1 *This is* / *This* Nele.
2 She's one of two **African** / **Africans** elephants in the zoo here.
3 She's **really big** / **big really**.
4 She's my **animal favorite** / **favorite animal** in the zoo.
5 I'm **happy very** / **very happy** that she has a baby.
6 She's **a good** / **good** mother.

3 a Match the pictures (a–f) to the descriptions (1–6).

1 This is my little brother. He's really f u n n y.   b
2 These are g_____t pictures from New York. It's a really c___l city.
3 These are my f_____e jeans. They're b___e and really n___e.
4 This is my favorite poster. It's a b____k and white picture of a f___t car.
5 This is our o___d refrigerator. It's n_____y and doesn't work very well.
6 This is my new laptop. It's a really cool J_p_____e one.

b Complete the sentences (1–6) with the correct adjectives.

4 Put the words in order to make sentences.

1 bike. / This / new / my / is   _This is my new bike._
2 are / clothes / These / nice. / really
3 my / French / This / pen pal, Vanessa. / is
4 house / isn't / My / big. / very
5 best friend / really / My / funny. / is

16

5 You're going to write a description of three things in your house. Make notes. Use the *Writing plan* to help you.

WRITING PLAN

1 What are the three things? Which rooms are they in? ☐

2 What colors, sizes, or age are they? ☐

3 Where are they from? ☐

WRITE AND CHECK

6 Write your descriptions. Write about 50 words. Then check (✓) the stages in the *Writing plan*.

››› Be a good classmate

1 Match the phrases (a–g) to the verbs (1–7).

It's good to …
1 be quiet *a*
2 throw ___
3 be ___
4 talk ___
5 listen ___
6 help ___
7 use ___

a when the teacher is talking.
b to the teacher.
c in a speaking activity.
d your phone after school but not in class.
e other students.
f nice.
g trash in the wastebasket.

2 Complete the **REFLECTION POINT** **with the words in the box.**

| all | ~~good~~ | learn | respect | students | teacher |

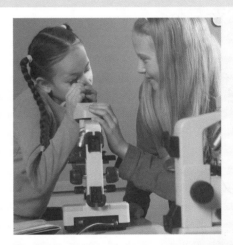

3 Match the solutions (a–f) to the situations (1–6).
1 Your classmate doesn't know how to do an exercise you can do.
2 The classroom isn't clean and neat.
3 You can't hear the teacher because it's noisy.
4 Your classmate doesn't talk to you in a speaking activity.
5 Your classmate uses his/her phone to text you in class.
6 You don't understand something.

a Be quiet, and ask other students to be quiet too.
b Help him/her. Show him/her how to do it.
c Throw trash in the wastebasket.
d Ask the teacher to explain.
e Don't use your phone in class.
f Say your part, and try to help him/her.

1 ___
2 ___
3 ___
4 ___
5 ___
6 ___
(b shown next to 1)

REFLECTION POINT

If you're a (1) *good* classmate, you (2) ___ the (3) ___ and other (4) ___ . When you're a good classmate, (5) ___ the students in the class can (6) ___ .

SCHOOL SKILLS

17

VOCABULARY REVIEW   UNIT 1

1 Write the colors under the pictures.

1 red   2 b_____   3 o_____   4 p_____ k

5 b_____ n   6 w_____   7 y_____   8 g_____

2 Match a–g to 1–7 to make words.

1 post   b   a bor
2 sand ____   b card
3 neigh ____   c glasses
4 sun   ____   d national
5 note ____   e wich
6 inter ____   f mate
7 class ____   g book

3 Choose the correct option, a, b, or c.

1 What's your ____ team?
  a quiet   ⓑ favorite   c nice
2 We have a lot of ____ in our city.
  a tourists   b visits   c countries
3 Throw your trash in the ____ .
  a game   b category   c wastebasket
4 International words are ____ in many different languages.
  a the same   b different   c like
5 There's a baby ____ in the zoo.
  a dinosaur   b elephant   c orange
6 Let's eat the ____ now.
  a neighbor   b Brazilian   c pizza
7 Washington, DC, is the ____ city of the USA.
  a capital   b big   c good
8 I never ____ a taxi to school.
  a do   b come   c take

ALL ABOUT ME

1 What country do you want to visit? Why?

2 What do you know about that country?

3 Who do you want to go there with?

GRAMMAR REVIEW

UNIT 1

1 a Complete the questions with Who, Where, What, When, or How.

1 _Where_ do you live?
2 _____ is your best friend?
3 _____ is your school?
4 _____ is my phone?
5 _____ is your nationality?
6 _____ is your birthday?
7 _____ old are you?

b Match the questions (1–7) in Exercise 1a to the answers (a–g).

a In Turkey. _1_
b Japanese. ____
c 13. ____
d Next to the station. ____
e Julia. ____
f Here it is. ____
g In March. ____

2 a Choose the correct options.

1 *Is* / Are this you / *your* pen?
2 Is / Are you one of the / – Tom's friends?
3 Is / Are that you / your in the picture?
4 Is / Are they she / her shoes?
5 Is / Are we in math class next?
6 Is / Are that you / your dog's house?

b Write short answers for questions 1–6 in Exercise 2a.

1 (X) _No, it isn't._
2 (✓) _____
3 (X) _____
4 (✓) _____
5 (X) _____
6 (✓) _____

3 Choose the correct options.

Kim's (1) *a* / the really good classmate. She (2) are / is my best friend too. (3) These / This is a picture of her in Canada on (4) their / our school trip in July. I love (5) – / the Ottawa. It's (6) an / a interesting city with a lot of things to do. Here's another picture. We (7) is / are in Toronto. It's (8) a / the great place.

4 Complete the text with the plural forms of the nouns in the box.

> activity ~~bus~~ class classmate
> day friend lunch

I live in Chicago, and I go to school in downtown Chicago. I take the bus to school. Our school (1) _buses_ are big and yellow. I have four (2) _____ – English, Spanish, math, and science. Then I go to the school cafeteria with my (3) _____. We eat our (4) _____ there. The food is OK. My school is very big. Big schools have a lot of (5) _____. My favorite activity is music class. I go to music class with my (6) _____. We go two (7) _____ a week – Tuesday and Thursday. It's fun!

19

2 PEOPLE
VOCABULARY 1 >>> Family

1 Complete the words in the sentences. Then find the adjectives in the word search.

My sunglasses are d i f f e r e n t from yours.

It's a q _____ place.

This is my n _____ phone.

He's a b _____ man.

It's a n _____ street.

She's very y _____ .

It's a h _____ day.

We have the s _____ bag.

We're s _____ .

What a n _____ dog!

You're a g _____ boy!

D	N	G	Q	B	Z	F	E	S
N	I	E	O	H	A	L	Y	I
O	S	F	W	O	B	D	O	M
I	A	R	F	I	D	L	U	I
S	M	M	R	E	Y	G	N	L
Y	E	R	W	U	R	E	G	A
J	O	R	Q	U	I	E	T	R
H	N	I	C	E	G	M	N	S
Z	K	W	Z	E	I	F	F	T

2 Which answer word from Exercise 1 needs *the*?

_____

3 Choose the correct option.
1 He's a *young* / *new* child.
2 This is my *new* / *young* phone.

4 Complete the sentences with the adjectives in the box.

good horrible new nice ~~quiet~~ same

1 Please be *quiet* . I can't hear.
2 I can't eat this food. It's _____ !
3 Do you like my _____ T-shirt?
4 You speak very _____ English.
5 We have the _____ shoes.
6 I love that old song. It's really _____ .

5 Complete the table with the words in the box.

brother ~~dad~~ father grandma grandpa mom mother sister

Male ♂	Female ♀
dad	

6 Write the names of the people in the family tree.

My sister's Sara. Our mom's Tina, and our dad's Omar. Our dad's parents are Paula (my grandma) and Luis (my grandpa). I'm Sara's brother, Marcos.

6 _Sara_

7 Decide whether the sentences are true (*T*) or false (*F*).
1 My grandfather is the father of my dad or mom. T/F
2 My sister is an only child. T/F
3 I have three mothers. T/F
4 An only child has no brothers or sisters. T/F
5 My grandmother is my grandma. T/F
6 My mom is my sister's mother. T/F

READING

>>> Read text messages

1 **Match the meanings (a–j) to the text message terms (1–10).**

1 4 _f_
2 UOK
3 HWK
4 IDK
5 THX
6 CU
7 NP
8 PLZ
9 ATB
10 YR

a No problem.
b See you!
c I don't know.
d thanks
e please
f for
g homework
h Are you OK?
i All the best.
j your

READING TIP
Look at the kind of text. It can help you understand what it's about.

2 **Read the text messages and match the people. Who messages who?**

1 Abel messages _____ . 2 Gail messages _____ . 3 Billy messages _____ .

Abel: Hi. Do u have time 4 a soda at about 6 on tues? ☺ ATB

Lili: THX 4 YR message. NP. CU at school on mon.

Anna: IDK. How about same time wed? That's better 4 me. x

Gail: Can't meet this weekend. A lot of of HWK. ☹

Billy: Plz call me. I need to talk to u now.

Dana: UOK??? Call u in 10 minutes.

3 **Match the meanings (a–j) to the emoticons (1–10).**

1 _b_
2
3
4
5
6
7
8
9
10

a I'm happy.
b I'm not happy.
c bicycle
d birthday
e I don't know.
f party
g present
h idea
i pizza
j sleepy

4 **Put the messages (a–h) in the correct order from old to new (1–8).**

a
Greg: It's Anna's 13th birthday party, Katie. Oh, cool – 🎂's here. NOW it's a good party!!

b
Greg: The best party? 😒 Boring …

c
Katie: Happy Birthday, Anna xxx 🎂 Hope you get a nice 🎁. ☺

d
Greg: Yes, come! 💡 Bring more pizza. ☺

e
Katie: ☺ Can I come now?

1 f
Laura: School tomorrow. ☹ But … this is the best party. I don't want it to stop.

g
Katie: Whose party is it? ☺ Greg, Laura? I'm not there – why not????

h
Anna: Thanks so much, Katie. I'm so lucky – look at my present from Mom and Dad: 🚲 ☺ Why aren't you here?

MOVE BEYOND
Use the internet to find more examples of "text speak." Then share them in your next English class. Here's an example: PCM = please call me.

21

GRAMMAR 1 *Have*

>>> Talk about your things, ideas, and problems

1 Complete the grammar table with the words in the box.

Do (x2)   Does   doesn't (x2)   don't   ~~have~~   has

Use *have* to talk about your things, ideas, and problems.
Affirmative
I/you/we/they (1) _have_ an idea.   He/She/It (2) _____ an idea.
Negative
I/you/we/they (3) _____ have a phone.   He/She/It (4) _____ have a phone.
Questions and short answers
(5) _____ I/you/we/they have a bike?   (6) _____ he/she/it have a bike?   Yes, I (7) _____ . / No, she (8) _____ .

2 ›› Choose the correct option.
1 I *doesn't* / *don't* have a smartphone.
2 We *don't* / *doesn't* have a dog.
3 They *don't* / *doesn't* have a cat.
4 He *has* / *have* two cars.
5 She *doesn't* / *don't* have a game console.
6 You *doesn't* / *don't* have a big family.
7 I *has* / *have* three sisters.
8 We *have* / *has* a nice house.

3 a Write questions. Use the correct form of *have*.
1 Clara / brother?
   Does Clara have a brother?
2 Mike / sister?
3 Clara / sister?
4 Mike / brother?
5 Clara and Mike / laptops?
6 they / tablets?
7 Clara / game console?

b ›› Look at the information about Clara and Mike. Write short answers to the questions in Exercise 3a.

	Brother	Sister	Laptops	Tablets	Game console
Clara	✗	✓	✗	✓	✓
Mike	✗	✓	✗	✓	✓

1 _No, she doesn't._
2
3
4
5
6
7

4 » **Put the words in order to make sentences.**

Dominic: have / you / Do / a / good movie / we can watch?
1 *Do you have a good movie we can watch?*

Joey: don't. / I / No,
2 _____

Dominic: you / have / DVD? / Do / a
3 _____

Joey: a / DVD of / *How to Train Your Dragon* / have / I
4 _____

Dominic: don't / that. / have / I
5 _____

Joey: anything / have / to eat? / you / Do
6 _____

Dominic: pizza. / I / have
7 _____

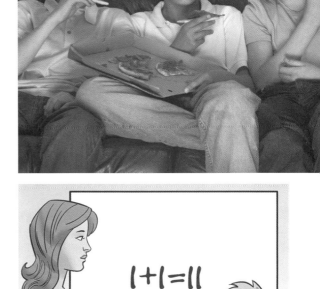

5 **Complete the conversations with *do* or *does* and *have*.**

1 ___*Does*___ John ___*have*___ a problem with math?
(✓) *Yes, he does.*
2 _____ Kate and Mary _____ the same last name?
(✓) _____
3 _____ Anna _____ a big house?
(✓) _____
4 _____ you _____ a favorite game?
(✗) _____
5 _____ we _____ a problem here?
(✗) _____
6 _____ I _____ the correct answers?
(✗) _____

6 »» **Write questions using *do* or *does* with *have* and short answers.**

1 you / your T-shirts
Do you have your T-shirts?

3 you / your sunglasses
_____

2 ✓ *Yes, I do.*

4 ✗ _____

5 the hotel / big rooms
_____

7 the hotel / a swimming pool
_____

6 ✓ _____

8 ✗ _____

9 your sister / my phone
_____

11 she / my camera too
_____

10 ✓ _____

12 ✗ _____

LISTENING

>>> Listen to a quiz show

1 **Match the pictures (1–5) to the descriptions (a–e).**

Shrek   Po   Spider-Man   Gollum   Gandalf

   a This person has long white hair.
   b This person has big ears. He has yellow teeth and big eyes.
   c This person has a big head and small ears. He has big black arms. His face is black and white.
   d We don't know what this person looks like. He has a mask on his face. His clothes are red and blue. He looks similar to a small animal with eight legs.
   e This person has big ears and a big nose. He's green. His good friend is an animal.

2 ▶07 **Listen to the Movie Quiz Show. Who said this – Mr. J, Alan, or Jill?**

1	Ready?	*Mr. J*	
2	No, that's wrong.		
3	I think it's …		
4	Those ears aren't his.		
5	Is it … ?		
6	Sorry …		
7	Correct.		
8	He has ears like that.		
9	Welcome to the Movie Quiz Show.		
10	Do you have any ideas?		
11	That's easy.		
12	The winner is …		

3 ▶07 **Listen again and check your answers.**

4 ▶07 **Listen again. Check (✓) the characters who are the correct answers in the quiz.**

   Gandalf ☐   Jackie Chan ☐   Po ☐   Spider-Man ☐
   Gollum ☐   Master Shifu ☐   Shrek ☐

5 **Choose the correct option.**

   1 Who has big ears?   Gandalf / *Gollum*
   2 Who is green?   Shrek / Po
   3 Who has a big head and black eyes?   Shrek / Po
   4 Who has white hair?   Gandalf / Spider-Man

6 **Who gets an answer wrong? Check (✓) the correct box.**

   a Jill ☐   b Alan ☐   c Jill and Alan ☐

7 ▶07 **Listen again and check your answers to Exercises 5 and 6.**

8 ▶08 **Look at the picture. Then listen to the riddle and choose the correct answer (a, b, c, or d). Who is it?**

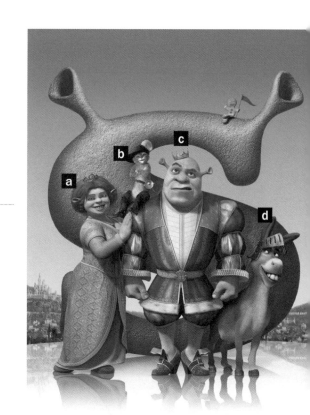

24

VOCABULARY 2

>>> Parts of the body

1 **Complete the words to answer the questions.**

1 You smell with this. What is it?	n*ose*
2 You look with these. What are they?	e_____
3 You speak with this. What is it?	m_____
4 You hear with these. What are they?	e_____
5 You run with these. What are they?	l_____
6 You have 32 of these. What are they?	t_____

2 **Match the pictures (a–f) to the parts of the body (1–6).**

1 arm — *b*
2 head
3 hand
4 foot
5 back
6 face

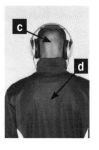

3 **Complete the description of the monster. Use the words in the box.**

| arms eyes feet legs mouth nose ~~head~~ |

1 This monster has one *head*.
2 It has four small _____.
3 It has three legs with big _____.
4 It has two long _____.
5 It has a small _____ with big teeth.
6 It has a funny _____.

WORDS & BEYOND

4 **Choose the correct option.**
1 What **today** / **(time)** is it?
2 We're all **smart** / **easy** in different ways.
3 See you in the **middle** / **morning**.
4 How do you **smile** / **spell** that in English?
5 Do you have a **park** / **family** in your city?
6 I don't have a **problem** / **present** for my mom's birthday.

5 **Complete the conversation with the words in the box.**

| ~~camera~~ contact list laptop smile text message wrong number |

Jules: Do you have a (1) *camera* on your phone?
Becki: Yes, I do. Why?
Jules: Take a picture of me.
Becki: OK. (2) _____ ! Oh, this is a good picture!
Jules: Now send it to me in a (3) _____ .
Becki: I don't have your phone number in my (4) _____ .
Jules: Email the picture to me, and I can see it on my (5) _____ .
Becki: I don't have internet now. Wait! Here is your phone number: 563-2359.
Jules: That's the (6) _____ ! My phone number is 563-2858!

GRAMMAR 2 *Whose?*, possessive *'s/s'*, and possessive pronouns

>>>> Talk about your things, family, and friends

1 Choose the correct options to complete the grammar table.

noun + 's
That's my (1) **mom's** / moms' car.
Regular plural noun + s'
That's my (2) *parents* / *parents'* car.
Whose + noun + question
Whose car (3) *that is* / *is that* ?

2 〉 Complete the table with possessive pronouns.

Possessive adjectives	Possessive pronouns
That's <u>my</u> pen.	That pen is (1) *mine* .
It's not <u>your</u> pen.	It's not (2) _____ .
That's <u>his</u> house.	It's (3) _____ .
That's <u>her</u> cat.	It's (4) _____ .
This isn't <u>our</u> dog.	It's not (5) _____ .
It's <u>their</u> bedroom.	It's (6) _____ .

3 a 〉〉 Make questions with *Whose* + *this* or *these*.

1 *Whose room is this?*

2 _____

3 _____

4 _____

5 _____

6 _____

b 〉〉 Matt has a room, pens, and jeans. Alicia has a phone, a bike, and books. Answer the questions in Exercise 3a.

1 *It's Matt's.*
2 _____
3 _____
4 _____
5 _____
6 _____

4 〉〉 Check (✓) the correct sentence. Correct the incorrect sentence. Write the correct word with an apostrophe (').

1 a My parents have a house near the ocean.
  b My **parents** house is very old.   ✓ *parents'*
2 a My two girls love animals.
  b My two girls names are Kim and Kara.
3 a My favorite grandpas name is Tom.
  b My grandfathers are Harry and Mick.
4 a Our neighbors dog is noisy.
  b Our neighbors don't like our dog.
5 a My favorite teams colors are black and yellow.
  b I like other teams too.
6 a The students have new tables and chairs.
  b The students classroom is great.

5 〉〉 Complete the text with the words in the box.

~~dad's~~   hers   mine   mom's   parents'   sister's

Happy Birthday to us!
It's my (1) *dad's* birthday today. He's 50. It's (2) _____ next week, and my (3) _____ birthday is next month. Mom's 45 now. My (4) _____ birthdays are on the same day of the month – the 12th. My little (5) _____ birthday is in July. (6) _____ is the same day as my grandma's.

6 〉〉〉 Write questions and answers. Use possessive 's (*Juanita's*) and possessive pronouns (*yours*).

1 dad?   Juanita
  Whose dad is he? *He's Juanita's.*
2 grandchildren?   my

3 brother?   Mario

4 mother?   our

5 child?   their

6 parents?   Kim

26

SPEAKING

>>> Talk on the phone

1 a Choose the correct options to complete the *Phrasebook*.

   b ▶09 Now listen and check.

2 ▶10 Listen to three conversations. Choose the correct answer a, b, or c.

Conversation 1
1 Which person is not there?
   a Mrs. Logan   b Lara   c Kim

Conversation 2
2 Mr. Phipps's problem is his …
   a phone.   b internet.   c spelling.

Conversation 3
3 Lee …
   a says Happy   b calls the   c doesn't
      New Year.   wrong number.   know Jess.

3 Choose the correct options to complete the conversations.

Conversation 1
Mrs. Logan: Hello.
Lara: This is Lara Hardy. Is Kim (1) *there* / *here* ?
Mrs. Logan: No, she isn't, Lara. (2) *Please* / *Sorry* , she's out.
Lara: (3) *Do* / *Can* you ask her to call me, (4) *sorry* / *please* ?
Mrs. Logan: Sure. (5) *Bye* / *Hello* , Lara.

Conversation 2
Mario: Good morning, Internet Answers. This is Mario.
John: Hello. This is John Phipps, and I have a problem with my internet.
Mario: OK, Mr. Phipps. How (6) *can* / *do* you spell your name?
John: P-H-I-P-P-S.
Mario: And your telephone number?
John: 210-769-1264.
Mario: Sorry, (7) *can* / *do* you repeat that?
John: 210-769-1264.
Mario: OK. Now what is the problem?

Conversation 3
Jess: (8) *Hello* / *Goodbye* .
Lee: Kung hei fat choi.
Jess: Sorry, I don't (9) *know* / *understand* . You have the wrong (10) *phone* / *number* .
Lee: No! It's me, Lee! Hi, Jess. It means "Happy New Year" in Chinese.
Jess: Oh, Lee! Thanks! Happy New Year to you too!

4 ▶10 Listen again and check your answers.

5 ▶11 Listen and repeat eight sentences from Exercise 4. Pay special attention to stress and intonation.

6 Write a phone conversation using phrases from the *Phrasebook*.

A:
B:
A:
B:
A:
B:

PHRASEBOOK

Make a call

Can I (1) *understand* / *speak to* … ?

Is this … ?

Is … there?

Can he/she (2) *call* / *repeat* me, please?

Answer a call

Can you (3) *spell* / *understand* that, please?

Sorry, can you (4) *call* / *repeat* that?

Sorry, I don't (5) *understand* / *speak* .

You (6) *speak* / *have* the wrong number.

Bye. / Goodbye.

WRITING

>>> **Write a description of a person**

1 **Complete the tips with the words in the box.**

REMEMBER HOW TO ...

use apostrophes

| possessive | ~~letter~~ |

- Use for a missing (1) _letter_ : he's
- Use with (2) _____ 's or s': *my brother's eyes, my sisters' eyes.*

2 **Read the description. Find the seven words that need apostrophes and write them correctly below.**

(Shakiras) my favorite singer. Her music is great. I love her songs, and she dances really well. Shes popular around the world, and Im one of her biggest fans. My sisters a big fan too, and she has all her songs on her computer. I dont have my own computer, but I have Dads old smartphone. Its great that I can listen to her whenever I want.

1 _Shakira's_   3 _____   5 _____   7 _____
2 _____   4 _____   6 _____

3 **Read the description of a person from a movie. Match him to the correct picture.**

He's a funny person. He has long brown hair, and he always has something on his head. I think he's about forty. He's smart and silly. He doesn't have any children. He likes the ocean and goes to many different places on his favorite kind of transportation – a ship or boat.

Who is he? Picture _____

4 **Read the description. Match the person to the correct picture.**

My favorite person is my sister. She's 15 years old. She has long brown hair. She's tall. She has a beautiful face and a nice smile. She's very intelligent. She's friendly. I love her very much.

Who is she? Picture _____

5 You're going to write a description of a person in a movie. Make notes. Use the *Writing plan* to help you.

WRITING PLAN

1 What does he/she look like? (age, hair, height) ☐

2 What things does he/she have? (special objects or possessions) ☐

3 What is he/she like? (personality, qualities) ☐

WRITE AND CHECK

6 Write your description. Write 30–40 words. Then check (✓) the stages in the *Writing plan*.

>>> Be friendly to other students

1 Complete the tips with the words in the box.

family   favorite   ~~hello~~   nice   phone

How to make friends.
Smile and say (1) _hello_ .
Ask questions about (2) _____ .
Say something (3) _____ .
Ask questions about (4) _____ movies or stars, clubs, and teams.
Ask for an address or (5) _____ number.

2 Put the words in order to make sentences.

1 your / like / I / bag.
   I like your bag.
2 have / you / Do / brothers and sisters?
3 live? / do / Where / you
4 favorite / Who's / your / singer?
5 you / on / sports team? / a / Are
6 Angie. / I'm / Hi,

3 Choose the correct options to complete the REFLECTION POINT.

4 Read what Angie says. What can you say to help her? Check (✓) the good ideas. Put an X next to the bad ideas.

I'm new at the school, and I don't have any friends there. I'm quiet, and it's not easy for me to make friends.

1 Say hello to people. ✓
2 Ask questions to see if you like the same things.
3 Don't say anything.
4 Ask about favorite things.
5 Listen to people's answers and say something nice.
6 Say what you don't like about a person.

REFLECTION POINT

It (1) *is* / *isn't* important to have a lot of friends. But new friends (2) *aren't* / *are* interesting. (3) *Talk* / *Don't talk* to people and make (4) *new* / *old* friends.

SCHOOL SKILLS

29

VOCABULARY REVIEW   UNITS 1 & 2

1 Match the pictures (a–h) to the things (1–8).

1 refrigerator *h*
2 trash _____
3 tourist _____
4 postcard _____
5 sandwich _____
6 notebook _____
7 camera _____
8 smile _____

2 Choose the correct options from the box below.

It's my sister's (1) _____ today. She's six years old, I'm 13, and our brother's 10. He's in the (2) _____ . We all have our birthdays in the (3) _____ month – June! Today we are at the (4) _____ . The weather is good, and my sister, Keira, wants to see the animals. She likes pandas, and they have a (5) _____ panda there. My (6) _____ animals are tigers. They're cool!

1	a present	**b** birthday	c special
2	a middle	b morning	c time
3	a similar	b different	c same
4	a zoo	b city	c album
5	a young	b right	c easy
6	a noisy	b favorite	c great

3 Complete the words in the text. Use FOUR people and FIVE places.

I love my (1) m *o* m and she loves (2) m _____ . I don't have a brother or a (3) s _____ r. I'm an only (4) c _____ d. I love my (5) h _____ e. My (6) r _____ m's great. We live on a nice (7) s _____ t near the (8) p _____ , but I go to (9) s _____ l on my bike.

4 Label the pictures.

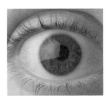
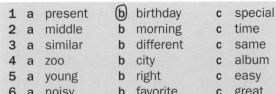

1 *ice cream*   2 p_____   3 e_____

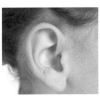

4 e_____   5 b_____   6 s_____

5 Find 11 words from Exercises 3 and 4 in the word search.

A	S	C	H	I	L	D
S	C	H	O	O	L	E
I	A	T	M	M	O	M
S	T	R	E	E	T	B
T	P	A	R	K	Y	I
E	Y	E	A	R	E	K
R	O	O	M	O	Y	E

ALL ABOUT ME

1 What's your favorite possession?

_____

2 What does it look like?

_____

3 Why do you like it?

_____

GRAMMAR REVIEW   UNITS 1 & 2

1 Complete the sentences with who's, whose, their, or there.

1 What's that over ___there___ ?
2 Is that _____ house?
3 _____ that girl?
4 _____ bag is this?
5 _____ your favorite singer?
6 I like _____ clothes.
7 _____ sunglasses are these?

2 Complete the postcard with the words in the box.

~~am~~   are   has   is (x2)   These   This

I (1) ___am___ in Bogota, Colombia. Bogota (2) _____ a big city. The people (3) _____ friendly. The city (4) _____ beautiful museums and parks. (5) _____ is a picture of Bolivar Square. (6) _____ people are tourists. They like Bogota. January (7) _____ a good month to visit.
Bye for now,
Jaime

3 Choose the correct options from the box below.

It's a boy! He (1) ___has___ big brown eyes and (2) _____ hair is white. He's (3) _____ new dog. We don't have a name for (4) _____ . (5) _____ Charlie (6) _____ good name for him? I (7) _____ know. I like (8) _____ name Sam.

	a		b		c
1	have	(b)	has	c	are
2	he	b	him	c	his
3	mine	b	my	c	me
4	he	b	his	c	him
5	Is	b	Are	c	Has
6	the	b	–	c	a
7	don't	b	not	c	no
8	a	b	the	c	one

4 a Complete the questions.

1 ___Are___ you Turkish?
2 _____ he have a brother or sister?
3 _____ you have a bike?
4 _____ he your classmate?
5 _____ is your favorite movie?
6 _____ is the movie theater?
7 _____ is her birthday?
8 _____ is her name?

b Match the questions (1–8) in Exercise 4a to the answers (a–h).

a No, he doesn't.   __2__
b January 10th.   ____
c Yes, he is.   ____
d No, I don't.   ____
e It's Nina.   ____
f It's *Gladiator*.   ____
g Yes, I am.   ____
h It's over there.   ____

31

3 ANIMAL MAGIC
VOCABULARY 1 >>> Pet animals

1 **Write the parts of the body. Then find the nine words in the word search.**

Dogs have two …
1 e y e s.
2 e____s.
Dogs have four …
3 l____s.
People have two legs and two …
4 f____t.
5 a____s.
Dogs have one …
6 f____e.
7 m____h.
8 n____e.
Dogs usually have a lot of …
9 t____h.

L	E	G	S	H	H	X	C
N	G	X	T	T	Q	M	L
N	E	U	E	N	I	D	W
D	O	E	F	A	I	V	V
M	T	S	Y	A	R	M	S
H	Y	S	E	E	C	S	T
W	J	F	X	C	S	E	X
I	F	F	E	E	T	M	N

2 **Match the pictures (a–g) to the pets (1–7).**

1 horse   b
2 fish   ____
3 bird   ____
4 mouse   ____
5 cat   ____
6 rabbit ____
7 dog   ____

3 **Read the clues and write the words. Use the words in the box.**

| bird | chicken | fish | hamster | ~~horse~~ | turtle |

1 I can't live in your house because I'm very big and tall.   *horse*
2 I give you eggs.   ____
3 I'm small. I have four legs, and you can have me in your bedroom. ____
4 I live in water and I can walk on land.   ____
5 I fly, and I can see you from up in the sky.   ____
6 I can't walk. I live in water.   ____

4 **Choose the correct options.**

Eva: I have two (1) *fish* / *fishies* named Wanda and Nemo.
Pete: What! Really? We have something in common. I have two (2) *mouses* / *mice* named Jerry and Mickey.
Eva: My brother lives in the country. He has a (3) *horse* / *horses* and about 30 (4) *chicken* / *chickens* .
Pete: That's a lot of animals. My sister lives in Los Angeles. She has two (5) *cat* / *cats* . She wants a big (6) *dog* / *dogs* , but her house is very small. I think she has (7) *mice* / *mouse* , but they're not pets!

32

READING

>>> **Read instructions**

1 Read the web page and answer the questions.
1. What is a kitten? It's a baby _____.
2. What can the vet give you? _____

READING TIP
Use pictures to help you understand new words.

TAKE CARE OF YOUR KITTENS
Use these instructions to help your kittens.

Give kittens a lot of toys, but don't give them string.

Don't pick them up all the time or hold them for a long time.

Give your kitten time to sleep.

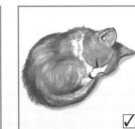

If a kitten doesn't have a mother, feed it with special kitten milk (not cow's milk). Get this special milk from your vet.

Don't let your kitten go behind your sofa.

Keep kittens with their mother for about the first 12 weeks.

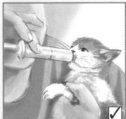

2 Read the website instructions again. Use the *Reading tip* to match the pictures (a–f) to the words (1–6).

1. string — e
2. hold _____
3. vet _____
4. feed _____
5. behind _____
6. sofa _____

a
b
c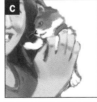
d
e
f

3 Decide whether these statements are true (*T*) or false (*F*).

1. It's good for kittens to play with a ball of string.   T/F
2. It's bad to hold kittens for a long time.   T/F
3. Baby kittens can drink cow's milk.   T/F
4. It's bad for kittens to be on a sofa.   T/F
5. Kittens don't need much sleep.   T/F
6. Kittens need their mother for about three months.   T/F

MOVE BEYOND

Use the internet to find out how to take care of some kind of pet. Write some *Do*s and *Don't*s. Share them in your next class.

Kind of pet: _____
Do _____ .
Do _____ .
Don't _____ .
Don't _____ .

33

GRAMMAR 1 Imperatives and object pronouns

>>> Give orders and instructions

1 **Choose the correct options to complete the grammar table.**

Imperatives
Affirmative
(1) *Close* / *Closing* your eyes.
Negative
(2) *Not* / *Don't* close your eyes.
Object pronouns
Look at …
(3) *I* / *me* .
(4) *you* / *your* .
(5) *he* / *him* .
(6) *her* / *she* .
(7) *us* / *we* .
(8) *they* / *them* .

2 **Write the pronouns in the box in the correct place.**

her him it me ~~them~~ us

1 I train dogs. It's easy to train ___them___ because they're intelligent.
2 Our family has a dog. Her name is Nina. We love _____ .
3 When we say "Nina!" she comes to _____ .
4 Nina likes to play ball with my brother. She plays with _____ .
5 Nina waits for _____ after school. I take her for a walk.
6 If you have a dog, be nice to _____ .

3 ❭ **Choose the correct option.**
1 *To come* / *Come in*, please.
2 *Please to sit* / *Sit in* that chair.
3 *Don't* *to eat* / *eat* in class.
4 *Not* / *Don't* use your phones in class.
5 *To go* / *Go* out now!
6 *Do no* / *Don't* put your bags on your desks.
7 *Writing* / *Write* your names on the test.

4 ❭ **Match the words/phrases (a–f) to the verbs (1–6).**

1 Stand   _b_   a your eyes.
2 Sit   _____   b up.
3 Open   _____   c at me.
4 Look   _____   d down.
5 Find   _____   e games.
6 Play   _____   f the answer.

5 a ❭ **Match the orders (a–f) to the pictures (1–6).**

1 _b_   2 ____   3 ____   4 ____   5 ____   6 ____

a fetch   c be quiet   e come here
b shake   d stand up   f sit down

b ❭ **Now match the words (a–d) to the verbs (1–4) to make instructions.**

1 Fetch   _b_   a move!
2 Shake   _____   b the ball.
3 Don't   _____   c down.
4 Lie   _____   d hands.

34

6 ›› **Complete the tips about having a dog. Use the affirmative or negative forms of the verbs in the box.**

| be | ~~give~~ | keep | play | take | say |

1 ✓ _Give_ it water and food every day.
2 ✓ _____ it for walks in the park.
3 ✗ _____ bad things to your dog.
4 ✓ _____ with it.
5 ✗ _____ it in a very hot place.
6 ✓ _____ nice to it.

7 ›› **Complete the conversations with object pronouns.**

Annie: I don't understand. I don't know how to do (1) _it_ (the exercise). Please help (2) _____ (Annie).
Ed: OK. Ask me about (3) _____ (the exercise). We can do it together.
Daniel: Look at those people. Do you know (4) _____ (the people)?
Isela: The boy's Harry. I know (5) _____ (Harry). He's in my math class. But I don't know (6) _____ (the girl). Who is she?
Daniel: Let's ask (7) _____ (the people) to come and sit over here with (8) _____ (Daniel and Isela). They don't look very happy.

8 ›› **Match sentences a–f to sentences 1–6.**

1 That's my book. _d_
2 John's very noisy. ___
3 We're late. ___
4 My kittens are very small. ___
5 Mary's not here. ___
6 Mark's a great player. ___

a Keep them with their mother.
b Call her on the phone now.
c Put him on the team.
d Please give it to me now.
e Please wait for us.
f Tell him to be quiet.

9 a ››› **Put the words in order to make sentences.**

1 right / Turn / here.   _Turn right here._
2 here. / park / Don't
3 fast / drive / Don't / here.
4 walk / Don't / dog / your / here.
5 Cross / here. / the street
6 help / for / here. / Call
7 the bus / here. / for / Wait
8 questions / here. / Ask

b ››› **Match the sentences (1–8) in Exercise 9a to the pictures (a–h).**

a

b

c

d 1

e

f

g

h

LISTENING

>>> Listen to a description of a room

1 Check (✓) the furniture you can find in a room.
   1 clock ☐
   2 bed ✓
   3 wall ☐
   4 table ☐
   5 chair ☐
   6 computer ☐
   7 floor ☐

2 ▶12 Listen to the conversation. Answer the questions.
   1 How many people are talking?   two
   2 Are they in their house?
   3 What animal is in the room?
   4 Are the people happy with the room?

3 ▶12 Listen again and check (✓) the things you hear.

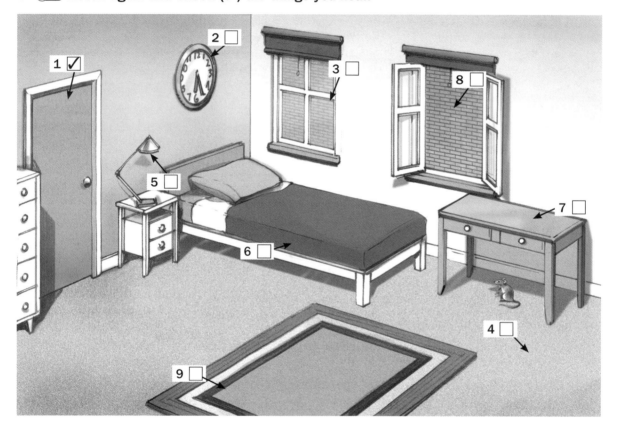

4 What problems are there with the room? Decide whether these sentences are true (T) or false (F). Listen again if you need help.
   1 There are noisy neighbors.   T/(F)
   2 There isn't a big bed.   T/F
   3 There's only one chair.   T/F
   4 There isn't a window.   T/F
   5 There isn't a light.   T/F
   6 There's a mouse.   T/F

5 a Complete the sentences with the words and phrases in the box.

   course   forget   is there   sorry
   there aren't   there's

   1 Of _course_ there's a bed.
   2 _____ any chairs.
   3 _____ a light here.
   4 _____ really a mouse?
   5 I'm _____ .
   6 Let's _____ about this room.

   b ▶13 Listen and check your answers.

36

VOCABULARY 2

>>> Things in your room

1 **Complete the sentences with the words in the box.**

bed   chair   desk   ~~picture~~   wall   window

1 I love this _picture_ .
2 I look out my _____ , and I can see trees.
3 My cat sometimes sleeps with me on my _____ .
4 I always sit on this _____ when I do my homework.
5 I do my homework at my _____ .
6 My favorite picture is up there on the _____ .

2 **Match the things (a–f) to the definitions (1–6).**

1 It usually has four legs.   _b_
2 It shows you the time.   ____
3 You use this to go into and out of your room.   ____
4 You stand on this.   ____
5 You can get information with this.   ____
6 It helps you see at night.   ____

a door
b table
c light
d computer
e floor
f clock

3 **Write three things from Exercises 1 and 2 that you can sit on.**

1 _floor_   2 _____   3 _____

WORDS & BEYOND

4 a **Match the words (a–e) to their opposites (1–5).**

1 horrible   _e_
2 easy   ____
3 quiet   ____
4 lie down   ____
5 wait   ____

a difficult
b noisy
c go
d stand up
e nice

b **Complete the text with words from Exercise 4a.**

Is it (1) _easy_ to take care of a hamster? Yes and no. My hamster, Cheri, (2) _____ and sleeps all day. She's very (3) _____ . I (4) _____ for her to wake up at night. Then she's (5) _____ . She eats and plays all night. It's (6) _____ to sleep with Cheri in my room. She likes to (7) _____ under my bed, but Mom doesn't like that. Cheri is small. She is 10 cm tall when she (8) _____ . Cheri's a (9) _____ pet.

5 **Complete the sentences below with the words in the box.**

cross   grass   neighbor   ~~perfect~~
shake   wait

1 What's your _perfect_ pet?
2 We play soccer on the _____ .
3 I can _____ hands with my dog.
4 Please _____ here for a minute.
5 Don't _____ the street if there are cars.
6 My new _____ is German.

GRAMMAR 2 *There is / there are*

>>> Describe a room

1 Complete the grammar table with *is*, *isn't*, *are*, or *aren't*.

There is/there are
Use *there is / there are* to describe what's in a place.
Affirmative
There (1) _is_ a dog on my floor. There (2) _____ some cats by the door.
Negative
There (3) _____ a bird by the window. There (4) _____ any fish on the table.
Questions and short answers
(5) _____ there a turtle in the classroom? Yes, there (6) _____ . / No, there (7) _____ .
(8) _____ there any rabbits in my hat? Yes, there (9) _____ . / No, there (10) _____ .

2 > Choose the correct options.

Leo: Look! (1) *There's* / *There are* a mouse in the house.
Amy: No, there (2) *is* / *isn't* . It's a toy.

Zoe: There (3) *are* / *is* three clocks on the wall.
Sara: Yes, but there (4) *isn't* / *aren't* any pictures.

Mia: (5) *There's* / *There are* my friend, Pablo.
Clara: Yes. (6) And *there's* / *there are* his sister.

Don: (7) *There's* / *There are* four parks near my house.
Jon: There (8) *isn't* / *aren't* one where I live.

3 a > Complete the sentences with *any* or *a*.

1 Are there _any_ tables?
2 Are there _____ chairs?
3 Is there _____ door?
4 Is there _____ computer?
5 Are there _____ windows?
6 Are there _____ desks?

b >>> Complete the short answers to the questions from Exercise 3a.

1 No, _there aren't_ .
2 Yes, _____ .
3 Yes, _____ .
4 No, _____ .
5 No, _____ .
6 Yes, _____ .

4 >>> Complete the funny story with *there's*, *there isn't*, *there are*, or *there aren't*.

(1) _There's_ a mouse in my house. But of course (2) _____ a horse. (3) _____ mice, and they're nice, but (4) _____ any rabbits. (5) _____ my dad – that's not bad, and (6) _____ my mom, and then (7) _____ some dogs and a cat, and that's that!

5 ▶14 Now listen and check your answers.

6 >>> Look at the picture. Write questions and short answers.

	Question	Answer
1	clock? _Is there a clock?_	_No, there isn't._
2	chairs?	
3	students?	
4	books?	
5	dog?	
6	cat?	

7 >>> Put the words in order to make questions. Then write the answers.

Lisa: (1) there / big / windows / Are / in the room?
Are there big windows in the room?
Mom: (2) ✓ _Yes, there are._
Lisa: (3) there / computer / Is / a / in the room?
_____
Mom: (4) ✗ _____
Lisa: (5) there / free / Wi-Fi? / Is
_____
Mom: (6) ✓ _____
Lisa: (7) there / Is / restaurant / a / at the hotel?
_____
Mom: (8) ✓ _____
Lisa: (9) there / parks / near the hotel? / Are
_____
Mom: (10) ✗ _____

SPEAKING

Ask for and give things

1 a Complete the conversations with the words in the box.

> are   borrow   course   ~~please~~   sorry   welcome

1
Andy: Dad, can I have some money, (1) _please_ ? I need some for lunch today.
Dad: Yes, of (2) _____ . Here you (3) _____ .
Andy: Thanks, Dad!
Dad: You're (4) _____ .

2
Ursula: Excuse me. Can I (5) _____ your pencil, Pam?
Pam: No, (6) _____ . I need it.

b Complete the *Phrasebook* with the words you used in Exercise 1a.

c ▶15 Now listen and check.

2 ▶16 Listen to three conversations. Check (✓) the things the people ask to have or borrow.

PHRASEBOOK

Ask for something
Can I have a/some ... , (1) _please_ ?
Excuse me. Can I (2) _____ your ... ?

Give something
Here you (3) _____ .

React
Yes, of (4) _____ .
Sure.
You're (5) _____ .
Thanks.
No, (6) _____ .

3 ▶17 Listen and repeat these sentences. Pay special attention to stress and intonation.

Conversation 1
Rob: Ben, can I borrow your bike?
Ben: No, sorry. It's mine.

Conversation 2
Mary: Mom? Can I have some money, please?
Mom: Yes, of course. Here you are.
Mary: Thanks.
Mom: You're welcome, Mary.

Conversation 3
Kate: Excuse me. Can I borrow your pen for a minute?
Dave: Sure. Here you are.
Kate: Thanks.
Dave: You're welcome.

4 Write a conversation using phrases from the *Phrasebook*.

A: (Ask for something) _____
B: (Give something) _____
A: (React) _____

WRITING

Write a note

1 Choose the correct option to complete the tips.

REMEMBER HOW TO …

write a note

1 *Write* / **Don't write** important information.
2 *Use* / **Don't use** imperatives (*Enjoy / Don't forget* …).
3 *Write* / **Don't write** long sentences.

2 Read these two texts. Check (✓) the one that is a note.

1
Hi, Julia. I can't come home for dinner tonight because I have a meeting at work. It's about the new plan for our parking lot. There's some great pasta and salad in the refrigerator. I hope you eat it all and enjoy it. Dad ☐

2
Zac! Call Zoe before 2 p.m. Remember: your piano lesson is at 3 p.m.! Dad ☐

3 Read the text and the two notes below. Check (✓) the best note (1 or 2) for the text.

Hi, Mark. I can't come home for lunch this afternoon because I have a meeting at school. The meeting is for all the teachers. There's some pizza and salad in the refrigerator. I hope you eat it all and enjoy it. Love, Mom

1
Mark. I'm at work this afternoon. Pizza and salad in the refrigerator – eat it all! Mom ☐

2
Hi, Mark. I'm meeting all the teachers. There's food on the top shelf. Lots of love. Mom ☐

4 Read this text and use the tips in Exercise 1 to rewrite it as a note. Use 10–15 words.

Hello, James. Our dog Max needs to go for a walk, and I'm at work. I have a lot of work to do. Can you take him to the park? Thank you very much. You're a very good boy. Dad.

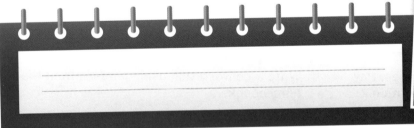

5 Read the notes (A–C) and answer the questions.

A
Tim, I'm at the office. The dog's food is on the table. Please give Gigi her food and take her for a walk. Thanks, Dad x

B
Harry, don't forget your piano lesson at 6. I'm at work, so take the bus. Enjoy, Mom x

C
Laura, I'm at Mike's (watching TV). The soccer game's on. There's some pasta in the microwave for dinner. See you later. Love, Tom.

1 Who's Gigi? _____
2 Where's Dad? _____
3 What's at 6? _____
4 Where's Mom? _____
5 What's on television? _____
6 What's for dinner? _____

6 You're going to write a note about a change of plan. Make notes. Use the *Writing plan* to help you.

WRITING PLAN

1 Who's your note for – a family member or a friend? ☐

....

....

2 What is the change of plan? Why is there a change of plan? ☐

....

....

3 What do you want the person to do? ☐

....

....

WRITE AND CHECK

7 Write your note. Write about 15 words. Then check (✓) the stages in the *Writing plan*.

>>> Prepare your things for school

1 Choose the best options to complete the REFLECTION POINT.

REFLECTION POINT

It's good to prepare your school things and do homework before (1) ⓑed / school .

It's (2) *good* / *bad* to keep your school things in a special place.

You can find them (3) *slowly* / *quickly* and not be late for school.

2 a ▶18 Listen to Harriet. Choose true (*T*) or false (*F*).

1 She prepares her school clothes before bed. Ⓣ/F
2 She finishes her homework before bed. T/F
3 She makes her lunch before school. T/F
4 She packs her bag before bed. T/F
5 She can't find her keys in the morning. T/F

b What do you think – is Harriet ready for school?

Harriet

3 Am I ready? Check (✓) the best option.

1 I eat something …
   a only after school. ☐
   b before school starts. ✓
2 I do my homework …
   a before school in the morning on the bus. ☐
   b at night after I eat at home. ☐
3 I prepare my school things …
   a in the morning. ☐
   b before bed. ☐

4 I keep my keys …
   a in my bag. ☐
   b on the floor. ☐
5 I prepare my clothes for school …
   a before bed. ☐
   b in the morning. ☐
6 I put my school books in my bag …
   a in the morning. ☐
   b at night. ☐

SCHOOL SKILLS

41

VOCABULARY REVIEW

UNITS 1-3

1 Choose the correct option, a, b, or c.
1 What do you want to eat for ___?
  a lunch   b morning   c basketball
2 Put your trash in the ___.
  a refrigerator   b wastebasket   c album
3 My ___ is six years old.
  a grandma   b dad   c sister
4 I can't hear anything here because it's really ___.
  a quiet   b noisy   c fantastic
5 I'm a(n) ___ child because I don't have brothers or sisters.
  a only   b one   c tall
6 Your birthday is your ___ day.
  a wrong   b friendly   c special
7 What's the name of the ___ you stay in?
  a car   b hotel   c market
8 How do you ___ that in English?
  a spell   b smile   c prepare
9 Is there any food in the ___?
  a wall   b desk   c refrigerator

2 Label the parts of the face.

1 eye
2 n____
3 e____
4 h____ d____
5 m____
6 t____

3 Write eight words for parts of the body, then find them in the word search.
1 E Y E
2 E_ R
3 M____ H
4 H____ D
5 T____ H (more than one)
6 L_ G
7 A_ M
8 F___ E

F	P	C	Q	H	H
A	E	H	T	T	L
C	V	U	E	Y	E
E	O	E	E	A	R
M	T	A	R	M	D
L	E	G	D	C	C

Hello! What's your name?

4 Choose the correct option.
1 The *Brazil* / *Brazilian* players are very good at soccer.
2 I go to *Turkey* / *Turkish* every year on vacation.
3 My pen pal is *Italy* / *Italian*. I help him learn English.
4 My *nose* / *teeth* are in my mouth.
5 There are some *horses* / *chicken* on my farm.
6 My pet *rabbit* / *bird* can talk. It's a parrot.

ALL ABOUT ME

1 What part of your face is like another person's in your family?

2 What is your favorite animal? Why?

3 What's your favorite hair color? Why do you like it?

GRAMMAR REVIEW

UNITS 1–3

1 Choose the correct options.

I (1) *have* / *has* a smartphone, but I (2) *don't* / *doesn't* have a computer. (3) *There* / *This* is a laptop in the house, and it's for all of (4) *we* / *us* . That's OK because I don't have any brothers or (5) *sister* / *sisters* . My mom and dad (6) *aren't* / *don't* use it a lot. I use (7) *the* / *these* laptop every day for homework and also for fun. Look. This is (8) *mine* / *my* favorite computer game.

2 a Complete the questions with the correct form of the verbs *be* and *do*.

1 *Do* you have a sister?
2 _____ you from Brazil?
3 _____ Juan have a brother?
4 _____ you have a favorite drink?
5 _____ Anna have a new friend?
6 _____ English grammar easy?
7 _____ we have the right answers?

b Match the questions (1–7) in Exercise 2a to the answers (a–g).

a No, I'm not. *2*
b Yes, I do. ____
c Yes, it is. ____
d Yes, we do. ____
e No, I don't. ____
f Yes, he does. ____
g Yes, she does. ____

3 Choose the correct options from the box below.

Kyle: I love (1) ____ . It's my favorite food. What about you?
Aaron: It's not (2) ____ . I don't like cheese.
Kyle: What's (3) ____ favorite food?
Aaron: I like anything that my dad makes. (4) ____ a great cook.
Kyle: (5) ____ can you make?
Aaron: Well, I often make (6) ____ salad. It's easy.

1	a	the pizza	**b**	**pizza**	c	an pizza
2	a	mine	b	me	c	my
3	a	you	b	your	c	yours
4	a	He's	b	His	c	He
5	a	Who	b	When	c	What
6	a	any	b	–	c	one

4 Choose the correct options from the box below.

Here's (1) ____ new pet. It's a snake. (2) ____ name is Jake. My brother has a hamster, and (3) ____ name is Hammy. Jake eats small animals, and we can't have (4) ____ in the same room. (5) ____ mom has a dog, and (6) ____ name is Daisy. Mom really loves (7) ____ . Dad has a kitten. (8) ____ name is Tom. Our family loves pets.

1	a	mine	**b**	**my**	c	me
2	a	Its	b	It's	c	It
3	a	him	b	he's	c	his
4	a	their	b	them	c	they
5	a	Our	b	Ours	c	We
6	a	she	b	hers	c	her
7	a	him	b	his	c	her
8	a	His	b	Its	c	Her

UNIT 4 PLAY

VOCABULARY 1 >>> Free-time activities

1 Write the words connected to free-time activities.

1 s_____r   2 s___p___g   3 i___r_e___   4 b___e

5 fr_____ds   6 m___v___s   7 b___k   8 m_____i

2 Match words a–f to words 1–6.

1 book — f — a movie
2 movie theater — b market
3 shopping — c computer
4 internet — d team
5 soccer — e people
6 friends — f paper

3 Complete the questions with the words in the box.

| bike   friends   internet   music   television   ~~video~~ |

1 What's your favorite _video_ game?
2 Can I borrow your _____, please?
3 What's on _____ tonight?
4 Do you like rock or pop _____?
5 Do you have a favorite website on the _____?
6 Where do you meet your _____ on weekends?

4 Choose the correct option.

1 Let's go out and ride our **bikes** / friends.
2 I can't go on the *music* / *internet*.
3 I meet my *friends* / *music* on Saturday afternoon.
4 My mom reads a new *movie* / *book* every week.
5 I can't play *soccer* / *shopping* today.
6 I go to the *movies* / *television* on weekends.

5 a Complete the sentences with the verbs in the box.

| go (x3)   listen   meet   read   ride   ~~watch~~ |

Hi. I'm Judy. I don't (1) _watch_ television, but I (2) _____ on the internet every evening. I don't (3) _____ books in my free time. I like to (4) _____ my friends and (5) _____ shopping with them or (6) _____ to the movies. I (7) _____ my bike in the park on Sundays, and I (8) _____ to music a lot on my phone.

b Check (✓) the things Judy likes, and put an ✗ next to the things she doesn't like.

1 bike ✓
2 shopping ☐
3 movies ☐
4 television ☐
5 books ☐
6 music ☐
7 internet ☐

44

READING

>>> **Read an article on a website**

1. **What do you think "handcycling" is? Check (✓) the answer.**
   1. a sport ☐
   2. a disability ☐
   3. a chair ☐

> **READING TIP**
>
> Before you read a text, think: "What's it about?" Read the title, headings, and first few sentences.

2. **Read the first two sentences of the text. Decide whether the sentences below are true (T) or false (F).**
   1. Handcycles are the same as bicycles. T/**F**
   2. There's only one kind of handcycle. T/F
   3. You can't use your legs to make a handcycle move. T/F

3. **Read the text and choose the correct option, a or b.**
   1. Are handcycles and wheelchairs the same?
      a yes **b** no
   2. What do handcyclists usually do?
      a put their hands on the wheels   b put their hands on pedals
   3. Who can use handcycles?
      a only people with disabilities   b anybody
   4. Is handcycling a Paralympic sport?
      a yes   b no
   5. Which picture shows a handcycle?
      a picture A   b picture B

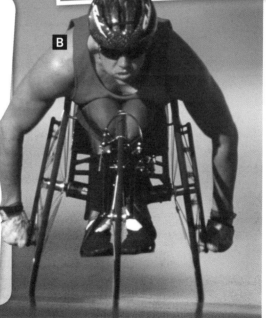

Handcycling

● What is a handcycle?
Handcycles are like bicycles, but they usually have three wheels. You use your arms, not your legs, to make the handcycle go.

● Is a handcycle a wheelchair?
No, it isn't. In wheelchair cycling, people put their hands on the wheels. In handcycling, they put their hands on pedals, like bicycle pedals, to go. In both sports there are three wheels.

● Who uses them?
Anybody can use a handcycle, but they are usually for people with disabilities.

● What can people do with a handcycle?
You can go on bike rides with friends and family and travel to a lot of different places. Handcycles are good exercise, and if you're very good, you can enter the Paralympics.

> **MOVE BEYOND**
>
> Use the internet to find three other wheelchair sports. Share what you find in your next English class.
>
> 1. _____
> 2. _____
> 3. _____

GRAMMAR 1 Can/can't

>>> Talk about the things you can do

1 Complete the grammar table with *can* or *can't*.

Can/can't
Affirmative
subject + *can* + verb   I (1) _can_ play tennis.
Negative
subject + *can't* + verb   I (2) _____ hear you.
Questions and short answers
Can + subject + verb   (3) _____ you play tennis?   Yes, I (4) _____ . / No, I (5) _____ .

2 >> Choose the correct option, a, b, or c.

1 I can't ___ you.
  a hearing   b to hear   (c) hear
2 Kim can ___ the guitar.
  a play   b plays   c playing
3 We can't ___ swimming today.
  a to go   b go   c goes
4 You can ___ sign language!
  a reading   b to read   c read

5 Dogs can't ___ some colors.
  a see   b sees   c to see
6 I can't ___ Japanese.
  a to understand   b understand
  c understanding
7 Leo can ___ three languages.
  a to speak   b speaks   c speak

3 a >> Write questions with *can*.

1 babies / walk?
 Can babies walk?
2 dogs / swim?
3 chickens / make eggs?
4 Ronaldo / play soccer?

5 Lady Gaga / sing?
6 fish / talk?
7 deaf people / hear?
8 you / play this sport?

b >> Answer the questions in Exercise 3a with short answers.

1 _No, they can't._   3 _____   5 _____   7 _____
2 _____   4 _____   6 _____   8 _____

4 » Complete the interview with *can* and *can't*.

What sports (1) _can_ **people in wheelchairs play?**
We (2) _____ play a lot of sports. We (3) _____ play all sports, of course, but here in Australia we (4) _____ choose from 14 sports, for example, basketball and tennis. You (5) _____ get special wheelchairs, and they're great.

What about you? (6) _____ **you play wheelchair basketball?**
No, I (7) _____, but I (8) _____ play tennis. I'm very good at it!

5 » What can and can't Yuki and Juan do? Complete the sentences.

	Speak Japanese	Ride a bike	Cook	Play tennis
Yuki	✓	✓	✗	✓
Juan	✗	✓	✗	✗

1 Yuki _can speak Japanese._
2 Yuki _____
3 Yuki _____
4 Yuki _____
5 Juan _____
6 Juan _____
7 Juan _____
8 Juan _____

6 »» Write three things in the table that you can do and three things that you can't do but want to do. Write full sentences using *can* and *can't*.

Can do	
1	
2	
3	
Can't do (but want to)	
4	
5	
6	

7 »» Write the class rules.

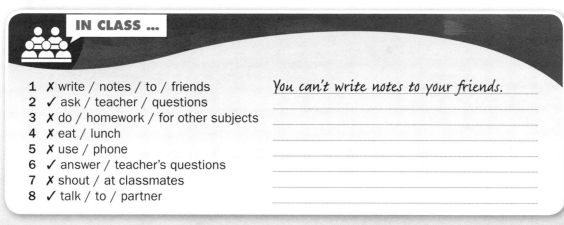

IN CLASS ...

1 ✗ write / notes / to / friends — _You can't write notes to your friends._
2 ✓ ask / teacher / questions
3 ✗ do / homework / for other subjects
4 ✗ eat / lunch
5 ✗ use / phone
6 ✓ answer / teacher's questions
7 ✗ shout / at classmates
8 ✓ talk / to / partner

LISTENING

>>> Listen to street interviews

1 **Imagine you're a musical instrument. What instrument are you? Why?**

   I'm a _____ because _____ .

   Example:
   I'm a saxophone because I'm cool and I love jazz music.

2 ▶19 **Listen to the interviews. Match the music (a–c) to the people (1–3).**

   1 Dwayne *c*   a traditional
   2 Yola _____   b rock
   3 Leo _____   c hip-hop

3 ▶19 **Listen again and answer the questions. Write *D* for Dwayne, *Y* for Yola, or *L* for Leo.**

   1 Who can play an instrument?   *Y* and *L*
   2 Who writes poems?   _____
   3 Who plays in a group?   _____
   4 Who likes old music?   _____ and _____
   5 Who writes songs?   _____
   6 Who plays in concerts?   _____

4 **Put the words in order to make questions.**

   1 music / do / listen / you / to? / What
     What music do you listen to?
   2 an instrument? / Can / play / you

   3 kind of / do / music / like? / you / What

   4 good singer? / Are / a / you

   5 musical? / you / Are

   6 groups? / about / What / new

5 **Choose the correct answers to the questions in Exercise 4.**

   1 (I listen to hip-hop.) / Yes, I listen to music.
   2 Yes, I do. / Yes, I can.
   3 I don't like rock. / I like traditional music.
   4 No, I'm not. / No, I can't.
   5 Yes, I am. / No, I can't.
   6 I like them. / I like it.

48

VOCABULARY 2

>>> Music

1 Write five kinds of music and five musical instruments, then find the 10 words in the word search.

Types of music
1 H _I_ P – H _O P_
2 R _ _ _ K
3 L _ _ _ N
4 C _ _ _ _ _ L
5 P _ _ _

Musical instruments
6 G _ _ _ _ R
7 V _ _ _ _ N
8 K _ _ _ _ _ D
9 D _ _ _ S
10 P _ _ _ _ O

D	H	C	P	W	T	N	N	L
R	R	I	K	O	I	X	A	G
U	O	Y	P	L	P	C	D	U
M	C	J	O	H	I	E	Z	I
S	K	I	B	S	O	R	D	T
O	V	G	S	I	M	P	X	A
G	L	A	T	I	N	T	I	R
C	L	P	I	A	N	O	S	O
C	K	E	Y	B	O	A	R	D

2 What instruments do these people play? Match the instruments (a–e) to the people (1–5).

1  _b_

3  ___

5  ___

2  ___

4  ___

a trumpet
b violin
c drums
d guitar
e piano

3 Complete the words in the text.

All for music & music for all!

Can you play an instrument? No? Why not learn with us? You can learn to play the

(1) _keyboard_ , (2) _____ ,

or (3) _____ and play different

kinds of music – (4) cl_____ ,

(5) p_____ , and

(6) r_____ . Come and join us.

Fridays at 5 p.m. in the music room.

WORDS & BEYOND

4 Complete the sentences with the words in the box.

| blind   dark   deaf   disability |
| ~~hearing aid~~   sign |

1 I can hear you with my _hearing aid_ on.
2 She can't see anything. She's completely _____ .
3 Can you read _____ language?
4 Don't shout! Be quiet! I'm not _____ .
5 I can see light and _____ things.
6 It's not easy when you have a _____ , but I enjoy life.

5 Complete the sentences with the verbs in the box.

| dance   pass   play   ~~sing~~   touch |

1 What songs can you _sing_ ?
2 Can you _____ your head with your foot?
3 Can you _____ me an apple, please?
4 Can you _____ to Latin music?
5 Can you _____ an instrument?

GRAMMAR 2 Simple present

>>> Talk about habits and routines

1 Choose the correct options to complete the grammar table.

Simple present
I/you/we/they + verb (+ object) I (1) **play** / **plays** Latin music.
he/she/it + verb + -s/-es He (2) **plays** / **play** the guitar.
I do homework. He (3) **dos** / **does** homework. I watch TV. She (4) **watch** / **watches** TV. I study hard. He (5) **studys** / **studies** hard. I have a new guitar. She (6) **has** / **haves** new drums.

2 >> Choose the correct option.

1 He *study* / *studies* music.
2 We *plays* / *play* in a group.
3 She *write* / *writes* the words.
4 He *makes* / *make* the music.
5 People *loves* / *love* our songs.
6 I *listen* / *listens* to different music.
7 We *practices* / *practice* a lot.
8 She *goes* / *go* to music lessons.

3 >> Choose the correct options from the box below.

Yes, sir. We're DOGGONE. I (1) ___ from a musical family. Yes, we all (2) ___ something musical. My uncle (3) ___ the piano, and my mom's on the drums. She (4) ___ how to hit those things! I (5) ___ . My brother Jeb (6) ___ fantastic things with his guitar, and we (7) ___ a concert every Friday and Saturday night at the DOGGONE Club. We (8) ___ you all to come along! Oh, yeah!

1	a	come	b	comes	c	coming
2	a	does	b	do	c	am
3	a	does play	b	play	c	plays
4	a	know	b	knows	c	knowing
5	a	am sing	b	sings	c	sing
6	a	do	b	does	c	doing
7	a	have	b	has	c	having
8	a	inviting	b	invites	c	invite

4 >> Complete the text with the verbs in parentheses + -s/-es.

My sister May (1) ___likes___ (like) classical music. She (2) ___ (play) the piano, and she also (3) ___ (sing). She (4) ___ (study) and (5) ___ (practice) every day after school. She (6) ___ (go) to piano lessons on Saturdays. She (7) ___ (teach) me the piano too.

5 >>> Complete the text with the simple present form of the verbs in the box.

go listen ~~spend~~ think try watch write

My brother Jim (1) ___spends___ all his free time with his guitar. He (2) ___ to traditional blues and jazz music and also (3) ___ his own songs. He (4) ___ videos of the great singers and guitarists and (5) ___ to copy them. I (6) ___ he's very musical, and we (7) ___ to all his concerts.

SPEAKING

>>> Tell the time

4

1 What time is it? Choose the correct option.

1
  a It's eleven thirty.
  ⓑ It's eleven o'clock.
  c It's twelve o'clock.

5
  a It's ten after eleven.
  b It's ten to twelve.
  c It's ten after twelve.

2
  a It's a quarter after six.
  b It's three thirty.
  c It's a quarter to seven.

6
  a It's twenty to nine.
  b It's nine to twenty.
  c It's twenty after eight.

3
  a It's five after three.
  b It's five after four.
  c It's five to four.

7
  a It's four after ten.
  b It's ten to four.
  c It's ten after four.

4
  a It's four thirty.
  b It's four o'clock.
  c It's five thirty.

8
  a It's a quarter to five.
  b It's a quarter after five.
  c It's a quarter after four.

2 ▶20 Listen and repeat the answers to Exercise 1.

3 ▶21 Listen and check (✓) the correct clock, a or b.

1 a   b   2 a   b   3 a   b   4 a   b

4 ▶22 Listen to three conversations. Check (✓) the correct statement.

Conversation 1
a There's time to get to the concert. ☐   b She's late for the concert. ☐

Conversation 2
a The movie is at 8:45 p.m. ☐   b The movie is at 9:15 p.m. ☐

Conversation 3
a Basketball practice is before lunch. ☐   b Basketball practice is after lunch. ☐

5 a Complete the *Phrasebook* with *time* or *It's*.

  b ▶23 Now listen and check.

6 ▶24 Listen and repeat the conversations. Pay special attention to stress and intonation.

Conversation 1
Jo: What time is it?
Mom: It's ten after eight.
Jo: Oh, no! We're late. The concert starts at a quarter after eight.
Mom: Relax. The concert is at eight thirty. We have time.

Conversation 2
Dan: What time's the movie?
Jo: It's at a quarter to nine.
Dan: Great. Let's go.

Conversation 3
Jo: Mom, what time is it now?
Mom: It's a quarter after one.
Jo: I have basketball practice at two o'clock.
Mom: OK. Have some lunch, and we can leave at ten to two. There's time.

PHRASEBOOK

Ask the time
What (1) _____ is it?
What (2) _____ 's the ...

Say the time
(3) _____ ... o'clock.
(4) _____ ten after/to ...
(5) _____ a quarter after ...
(6) _____ a quarter to ...
(7) _____ at ...

7 You and your friend want to go to the movies. Write the conversations using phrases from the *Phrasebook*.

1 **A:** (Ask the time)   2 **A:** (Ask what time the movie is)

  B: (Say the time)   **B:** (Say the time)

51

WRITING

>>> **Write an email**

1 Match the examples (a–e) to the rules (1–5).

REMEMBER HOW TO …

use capital letters

1	At the beginning of a sentence.	b
2	For the pronoun "I."	
3	For the names of people and places.	
4	For countries, nationalities, and languages.	
5	For days of the week.	

a   She plays the piano on Thursdays.
b   How are you?
c   Now Anna lives on Main Street.
d   He's Spanish. He's from Barcelona.
e   I'm here.

2 Circle the capital letters in the email.

> (H)i Graciela,
> It's great to hear from you. Your English is very good. It's fantastic that we can meet on Saturday. I think we can go out at night. Call me when you get to San Diego. My mom can pick you up at the Solana Beach bus station.
> Love,
> Carole

3 One word in each sentence needs a capital letter. Write the word.

1 The book says the famous Pyramids of Giza are in egypt. _Egypt_
2 Look. Here's a picture of the glass pyramid at the Louvre Museum in paris, France. _____
3 where is Egypt? _____
4 It's in Africa, i think. _____
5 Yes, you're right. I remember. Uncle john goes there every year. _____
6 This report is for thursday, right? _____

4 Put the words in order to make an email. Use capital letters where you need to.

anna, / hi
1 _Hi Anna,_
again. / to hear from you / great / it's
2 _____
my first concert / well, I have / on saturday.
3 _____
songs. / traditional spanish / we sing
4 _____
a little nervous / about it. / i'm
5 _____
wishes, / best
6 _____
antonio
7 _____

4

5 You're going to write an email about your activities on weekends. Make notes. Use the *Writing plan* to help you.

WRITING PLAN

1 Who are you writing to? ☐

....

....

2 What interesting things do you do on weekends? Where do you go? ☐

....

....

3 Who do you go with? ☐

....

....

4 What do you want to ask your friend? ☐

....

....

WRITE AND CHECK

6 Write your email. Write about 50 words. Then check (✓) the stages in the *Writing plan*.

⟫⟫⟫ Write down your homework

1 Check (✓) the things you can do to remember your homework.

1 Write a note on your phone. ✓	4 Write it on the board. ☐
2 Put it on the school website. ☐	5 Tell a friend. ☐
3 Write it on a piece of paper. ☐	6 Write it in a homework planner. ☐

2 Match the answers (a–c) to the questions (1–3).

1 What's the homework?   *c*   a Monday, October 12
2 What book(s) do I need? ......   b Workbook
3 When is it due? ......   c Workbook page 48, exercises 1, 2, 3

3 Read the `REFLECTION POINT`. Then check (✓) the information you need for a writing assignment.

1 How many words do I need to write? ✓
2 What's the subject? ☐
3 What time is it now? ☐
4 What kind of writing is it (note, email, story …)? ☐
5 Who do I write to/for (my teacher, a friend, in a blog …)? ☐
6 Why do I write this? ☐
7 When is it due? ☐
8 Who can help me with the homework? ☐

4 ▶25 Listen and complete the student's homework planner with words you hear.

Task:	Write an (1) ___essay___ on the (2) ....
Books and help:	Read unit (3) .... and use the internet to find information.
Where:	Write your essay in your (4) ....
When for:	Do homework by (5) ....

REFLECTION POINT ≪

It's important to write down your homework. Always ask: *What's the task? What do I need? Where do I do it? When is it due?*

SCHOOL SKILLS

VOCABULARY REVIEW   UNITS 1-4

1 Choose the correct option.
1 Put your trash in the *wastebasket* / *refrigerator*.
2 Eat an *apple* / *album* every day.
3 Many *vacations* / *tourists* go to other countries.
4 *Smile* / *Spell* and look at the camera.
5 That's a great *idea* / *problem*.
6 Sorry. You've got the *wrong* / *smart* number.
7 Sit down on the *wall* / *chair* there.
8 Let's *cross* / *shake* hands and forget about it.

2 a Write eight adjectives. Then find them in the word search.

1 E A S Y
2 O _ _ D
3 L _ _ _ T
4 D _ _ K
5 T _ _ L
6 Y _ _ _ G
7 N _ _ _ Y
8 N _ E

N	O	I	S	Y	E
I	L	I	G	H	T
C	D	A	R	K	A
E	A	S	Y	E	L
Y	O	U	N	G	L

b Complete the sentences with the words from Exercise 2a.
1 John is *tall* for his age. He's only 12 and he's 1.80 meters tall.
2 This homework is very _____ . I can finish it in five minutes.
3 In Alaska it gets _____ very early in winter.
4 In summer, it's _____ before 7 in the morning.
5 Joanna is my best friend because she is a very _____ person.
6 My phone is very _____ . I need a new one.
7 My mother is a teacher. She teaches _____ children.
8 It's too _____ in here. Stop shouting, everyone!

3 Choose the best options from the box below.
I (1) ___ my (2) ___ in the park with my friends (3) ___ Saturday mornings. I usually go to the (4) ___ and watch a movie at night. I (5) ___ soccer on Sunday mornings. My (6) ___ wins a lot of games. Of course, I also (7) ___ my homework so I'm ready for (8) ___ on Monday.

1	a dance	**b ride**	c sing
2	a car	b train	c bike
3	a at	b in	c on
4	a movies	b museum	c theater
5	a go	b work	c play
6	a team	b title	c top
7	a make	b do	c am
8	a neighbors	b school	c home

ALL ABOUT ME

1 **What's your favorite thing to do on Sunday?**

2 **What's your favorite kind of music?**

3 **What's your favorite animal?**

GRAMMAR REVIEW

UNITS 1-4

1 Decide which sentences are correct. Check (✓) the correct ones, and correct the incorrect ones (write *do*, *does*, *have*, or *has*).

1 Does you have any pets? ☐ *Do*
2 She has a sister. ☐
3 They don't have any sisters. ☐
4 Does you have a big family? ☐
5 We always has a lot to talk about. ☐
6 John and Paul don't have any pets. ☐
7 She have a new car. ☐
8 My grandparents has a house in the country. ☐

2 Complete the sentences with *'s*, *isn't*, *are*, or *aren't*.

1 There ___are___ a lot of hotels in my town. (✓)
2 There _____ some nice restaurants. (✓)
3 My dad _____ a chef in a restaurant. (✓)
4 There _____ an outdoor movie theater in the summer. (✓)
5 There _____ a lot of stores for tourists. (✓)
6 There _____ many people here in the winter. (✗)
7 There _____ a theater. (✗)
8 There _____ some great beaches. (✓)

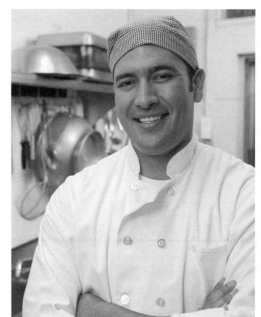

3 Choose the correct options.

1 Hi. Are you in the car with your mom? — Yes, I **am** / are . Thanks.
2 I can't hear you very well. Can you hear me? — Yes, I **can** / **can't** .
3 Do you have the party things? — Yes, we **do** / **don't** .
4 Can you meet me at the Nice Café? — Yes, **can we** / **we can** .
5 Can you be there at 6:00? — No, **you** / **we** can't.
6 Can you be there at 6:30, then? — Yes, we **can** / **am** . See you there.

4 Complete the text with the verbs in the box.

| ask | dance | put | run | see | sit | ~~take~~ |

This is the plan. We (1) ___take___ the cake to the café. We (2) _____ the cake on the table. We (3) _____ our friends to be quiet. When we (4) _____ Maria at the door of the café, we all (5) _____ out and sing "Happy Birthday." Then we (6) _____ down and eat the cake. Then we (7) _____ . My brother Diego's the DJ.

5 Choose the correct options.

Hi Dad. (1) **There's** / There are a problem with the music at the party. Diego's (2) **this** / **here** , but his laptop isn't working. What (3) **are** / **do** we do now? (4) **Help** / **Helps** me, Dad! Can you (5) **come** / **to come** with your guitar? You know we (6) **love** / **loves** your songs. The Nice Café (7) **is** / **are** on Green Street. Thanks!

55

UNIT 5

OTHER WORLDS

VOCABULARY 1 >>> Jobs

1 Match the sentences (a–h) to the places (1–8).

1	hospital	*h*	a	*I have 600 chickens here.*
2	store		b	*Do you have a room for tonight?*
3	hotel		c	*My team plays on Sundays.*
4	restaurant		d	*I don't have homework today.*
5	soccer stadium		e	*Can I have steak, fries, and salad, please?*
6	school		f	*What time is the show?*
7	farm		g	*Let's get some milk and fruit.*
8	theater		h	*What's the problem with your leg?*

2 Answer the questions with the places from Exercise 1.

1 Where can you go to eat with friends?   *restaurant*
2 Where can you see animals?
3 Where can you watch a game?
4 Where can you see a play?
5 Where do people go when they have a problem with their body?
6 Where can you stay on vacation?
7 Where can you buy a lot of things?
8 Where do children learn?

3 Match the jobs (a–d) to the descriptions (1–4). Then find the six jobs (a–d) in the word search.

1 I work with animals in the country. *c*
2 I work in a restaurant.
3 I work in a theater.
4 I work in a hospital.

a waiter / cook
b actor
c farmer
d doctor / nurse

N	A	D	J	A	W
U	C	O	O	K	A
R	T	C	B	I	I
S	O	T	S	N	T
E	R	O	L	G	E
F	A	R	M	E	R

4 Who says these things? Match the people in the box to the sentences (1–8).

~~actor~~ cook nurse receptionist sales clerk
soccer player teacher waitress

1 *My next movie opens in December.*   *actor*

2 *Take this medicine and don't go to school.*

3 *Please open your books to page 10.*

4 *Would you like a drink with your food?*

5 *Your room's Number 41. Here are the keys.*

6 *My shirt number is seven. That's my lucky number.*

7 *Take this food to the people at table six.*

8 *These shoes are 35 dollars, and those are 40.*

56

READING

>>> **Read a questionnaire**

1 a Read the instructions for the questionnaire.

> How active are you? Read this questionnaire and find out. Read each question. Then choose the answer that is usually true for you. When you finish, count the number of A, B, or C answers and calculate your score.

b Put the instructions in the correct order.

a Decide your answer. _____
b Circle your answer. _____
c Read the question.   1
d Calculate your score. _____

2 Read and do the questionnaire.

> Exercise is very important. How active are you? Do you need to move more often? Take this quiz and find out.
>
> 1 When I have some free time, I like to …
>   a turn on the TV, watch a DVD, or listen to my favorite music.
>   b take the dog out for a short walk or help around the house.
>   c go outside and walk, run, ride my bike, or play a sport with friends or family.
> 2 I can run up and down the stairs four times with a heavy backpack and …
>   a Well … in fact, I can't. Up and down one time is enough!
>   b I'm very tired after I do that.
>   c I don't feel tired at all.
> 3 I do some kind of intense physical activity …
>   a about one time every two weeks.
>   b two or three times a week.
>   c nearly every day.
> 4 My general attitude about exercise/doing sports is …
>   a I don't like it, and I try to do as little as possible.
>   b It isn't much fun, but it's OK sometimes.
>   c I enjoy it and do as much as I can!

3 Read the instructions to score your results. Read what your score means. Are you getting enough exercise?

> Give yourself 1 point for each A answer, 2 points for each B answer, and 3 points for each C answer.
>
> My score is _____ .
>
> What your score means:
> 10–12 Wow! You're a very active person! You're keeping your body fit and healthy!
> 7–9 You can do better. Remember, regular physical activity is good for you.
> 4–6 You need to rethink your activities. Your lifestyle isn't healthy. Get up and move!

4 Read one more question on the questionnaire. Complete the answer choices with the words in the box.

| active   board games   walk |

> 5 If my friends want to do exercise or play sports, I …
>   a never participate. I prefer to play _____ .
>   b sometimes join them if we go for a _____ .
>   c always go with them. I like to be _____ .

MOVE BEYOND

Write three questions for a questionnaire. Find out what kind of games your classmates like playing. Ask your questions in your next English class.

57

GRAMMAR 1 Simple present

>>> Ask and answer questions about habits and routines

1 Complete the grammar table with the words in the box.

do (x4)   don't (x2)   does (x2)   doesn't (x2)   ~~likes~~

Affirmative
I like my work.
She (1) _likes_ her work.

Negative
I (2) _____ like my work.
She (3) _____ like her work.

Questions	Answers
(4) _____ you like your job?	Yes, I do. / No, I (5) _____ .
(6) _____ she like her job?	Yes, she does. / No, she (7) _____ .
(8) _____ people help you in your job?	Yes, they (9) _____ . / No, they don't.
(10) What _____ you like about your job?	I like the people there.
(11) When _____ he get home?	He gets home at six o'clock.

2) Choose the correct option, a, b, or c.
1 I ___ know a famous person.
   (a) don't   b not   c doesn't
2 He ___ play soccer.
   a doesn't   b no   c don't
3 They ___ work in the theater.
   a doesn't   b don't   c not
4 We ___ go out on Monday night.
   a don't   b not   c doesn't
5 She ___ like restaurants.
   a not   b don't   c doesn't
6 I ___ have a problem with this exercise.
   a doesn't   b no   c don't
7 You ___ believe me!
   a not   b don't   c doesn't

3) Choose the correct options.
Sam: (1) *Are* / *Do* you work in a hotel?
Rita: Yes, I (2) *am* / *do* .
Sam: What (3) *you do* / *do you* do?
Rita: I help people, but I (4) *doesn't* / *don't* work at a desk.
Sam: (5) *Do* / *Does* people ask you questions?
Rita: Yes, they (6) *do* / *don't* .
Sam: (7) *Do* / *Does* you work in their rooms?
Rita: No, (8) *I'm not* / *I don't* . I'm a waitress in the hotel restaurant.

4 a) Choose the correct question word.
1 (Where) / When do you live?
2 Which / What do you have for lunch?
3 When / What do you finish school?
4 What / Who does your dad do?
5 Where / What does your mom do?
6 Where / Who does she work?
7 What / When time do they get home?

b) Match the questions (1–7) in Exercise 4a to the answers (a–g).
a She's a receptionist.   5
b He's a waiter.   ____
c I finish at 3:30.   ____
d She works downtown.   ____
e I live in San Antonio.   ____
f They get home at 4:00.   ____
g I have a salad, a sandwich, and fruit.   ____

5 a)) Correct the mistakes in the questions.
1 Does they go on vacation to Spain?
   Do they go on vacation to Spain?
2 Where she goes on vacation?
   _____
3 Does he works in a hotel?
   _____
4 When do he has free time?
   _____
5 Do she goes to restaurants?
   _____
6 What they likes to eat?
   _____
7 You drinks coffee?
   _____
8 Why I do make mistakes?
   _____

b)) Match four questions in Exercise 5a to the answers (a–d).
a Yes, I do.   7
b Yes, he does.   ____
c No, they don't.   ____
d Yes, she does.   ____

58

6 a ›› **Complete the questions about Jorge's job with *Do* or *Does*. Then write short answers.**

1 *Does* he work in a hospital? ✓
   Yes, he does.
2 _____ he help doctors? ✗
3 _____ people ask him for help? ✗
4 _____ he answer phone calls? ✗
5 _____ he work with food? ✓
6 _____ people in the hospital need him? ✓

b What is Jorge's job? Choose picture 1, 2, 3, or 4. _____

7 ››› **Write interview questions and answers.**

Interviewer: you / play tennis / ?
(1) *Do you play tennis?*
Marcus: ✓ (2) *Yes, I do.*
Interviewer: you / good / at tennis / ?
(3) _____
Marcus: ✓ (4) _____
Interviewer: you / lose / a lot of games / ?
(5) _____
Marcus: ✗ (6) _____
Interviewer: you / have / a good coach / ?
(7) _____
Marcus: ✓ (8) _____ His name's Bob Sims.

Interviewer: Marcus / practice a lot / ?
(9) _____
Bob Sims: ✓ (10) _____
Interviewer: Marcus / win a lot of big matches / ?
(11) _____
Bob Sims: ✓ (12) _____
Interviewer: Marcus / play computer games in his free time / ?
(13) _____
Bob Sims: ✓ (14) _____
Interviewer: Marcus / a bad student / ?
(15) _____
Bob Sims: ✗ (16) _____

LISTENING

>>> **Listen to a radio show**

1 ▶26 **Listen to the host of a radio show and choose the correct option, a or b.**

   1 What time is it?
      a nine o'clock in the morning   b nine o'clock at night
   2 What day is it?
      a Saturday   b Sunday
   3 What does the host want to know?
      a What's your favorite day?   b What do you usually do on Sunday?
   4 What does the host want people to do?
      a call the radio show   b text the radio show

2 **Check (✓) what YOU think is different about Sundays.**

	Me	Sharon	David
1 get up late			
2 eat with all the family			
3 go out with friends			
4 have a good breakfast			
5 have time to play sports			
6 don't do homework			

3 ▶27 **Now listen to the radio show and check (✓) what Sharon and David say.**

4 ▶27 **Listen again. Decide if the statements are true (T) or false (F).**

   1 Sharon has a good breakfast on school days.   T/F
   2 She goes to the park or to a museum in the afternoon. T/F
   3 She goes to bed at ten o'clock.   T/F
   4 David takes a shower in the morning.   T/F
   5 He plays soccer at two o'clock.   T/F
   6 He meets his friends.   T/F

5 ▶27 **Listen again. Check (✓) the daily routine activities you hear.**

   1 do homework   ✓   5 go to school   ☐
   2 go to bed   ☐   6 have dinner   ☐
   3 take a shower   ☐   7 get up   ☐
   4 go home   ☐

60

VOCABULARY 2

>>> Daily activities

1 Choose the correct option.
1. I *do* / (*go*) to bed.
2. I *do* / *take* a shower.
3. I go to *home* / *school* .
4. I get *up* / *shower* .
5. I do my *homework* / *home* .
6. I *watch* / *play* TV.
7. I *go* / *finish* school.
8. I *do* / *have* breakfast.

2 Match the times (a–c) to the meals (1–3).
1. dinner   *c*
2. breakfast   ____
3. lunch   ____
a. 7:30 in the morning
b. 1:00 in the afternoon
c. 7:30 p.m.

3 a Complete the text with the words in the box.

do ~~get~~ go (x3) have (x2)

On school days I (1) *get* up at ⏰ ,

and I (2) _____ breakfast at ⏰ .

Then I (3) _____ to school at ⏰ .

I (4) _____ home from school at ⏰

and (5) _____ my homework from ⏰ to ⏰ .

Then I (6) _____ dinner at ⏰ and

(7) _____ to bed at ⏰ .

b Write the times in the text.
1. *seven-thirty*
2. _____
3. _____
4. _____
5. _____ , _____
6. _____
7. _____

WORDS & BEYOND

4 Complete the sentences with the words in the box.

| active believe count create ~~mystery~~ order |
| perfect questionnaire routine smile |

1. We don't know what he does. It's a *mystery* .
2. Waiter! Can I _____ now, please?
3. I like to _____ things with my hands.
4. What's your _____ job?
5. I can't _____ we are the number 1 team!
6. I don't have a daily _____ .
7. Please answer this _____ .
8. Are you ready for the picture? _____ !
9. Can you _____ from one to ten in German?
10. I like to exercise and be _____ .

GRAMMAR 2 Adverbs of frequency

>>> Say how often you do things

1 Complete the table with adverbs of frequency.

always ~~never~~ often

Adverbs of frequency
0%   (1) _never_
sometimes
(2) _____
usually
100%   (3) _____
Word order
adverb + verb
I always listen to the radio.
We never go to school on Sunday.
She sometimes helps her mom cook.

2 >>> Choose the best adverb to complete each sentence. Use the frequencies (%) to help you.

1. (0%)   I **never** / always go to bed early.
2. (30%)   I sometimes / usually eat fish.
3. (80%)   I usually / often play tennis on weekends.
4. (100%) I always / usually meet my friends on weekends.
5. (60%)   I often / usually do my homework before dinner.
6. (30%)   I sometimes / never read books.
7. (0%)   I always / never take a shower in the morning.

3 >>> Put the words in order to make sentences.

1. sleeps / She / always / late.
   She always sleeps late.
2. never / He / soccer. / plays
3. often / They / forget / to call.
4. in / my bedroom. / my homework / I / usually / do
5. never / answers / She / my emails.
6. my phone / have / always / I / on.
7. watch / sometimes / I / DVDs.
8. usually / He / works / at / night.

4 >> Look at the table and the adverbs. Write what is true for the people.

	Bike
Will	✓✓
Sam	✓
Alex	✓✓✓✓
Ellie	✗
Paula	✓✓✓

Use:
always (✓✓✓✓)
usually (✓✓✓)
often (✓✓)
sometimes (✓)
never (✗)

How often do you ride your bike to college?

1 Will — _I often ride my bike to college._
2 Sam
3 Alex
4 Ellie
5 Paula

5 >>> Rewrite the sentences. Put the adverbs in parentheses in the correct place.

1. He listens to the radio. (often)
   He often listens to the radio.
2. They read books on vacation. (sometimes)
3. I have fruit for breakfast. (always)
4. Ruth walks to school. (often)
5. My grandmother goes for a walk at night. (usually)
6. Jack helps his father cook food. (usually)
7. They watch TV in the morning. (never)

SPEAKING

5

>>> **Ask for and give reasons**

1 Match the reasons (a–d) to the questions (1–4).

1 Why do we study English? *d*
2 Why isn't your homework here? ____
3 Why can't you stop talking? ____
4 Why are you happy? ____

a Because it's at home.
b Because I have a lot to say.
c Because it's my birthday.
d Because it's an international language.

> **PHRASEBOOK**
>
> **Asking for reasons**
> *Why?*
> *Why not?*
>
> **Giving reasons**
> Because I / you / it ...

2 Choose the best question.

1 There aren't any taxis. *Why? / (Why not?)*
2 I can't listen to classical music. *Why? / Why not?*
3 Can you come here, please? *Why? / Why not?*
4 I don't have any more money. *Why? / Why not?*
5 Give that to me. *Why? / Why not?*

3 ▶28 Listen to three conversations. Check (✓) the people that ask for help.

Conversation 1		Conversation 2		Conversation 3	
Pete	✓	Amy	☐	Alfie	☐
Mr. Green	☐	Mom	☐	Rachel	☐

4 ▶28 Listen again. What do the people want help with?

Conversation 1
a a car b (a bike)
Conversation 2
a furniture b glasses
Conversation 3
a a friend b a word

5 ▶29 Listen and repeat these sentences. Pay special attention to stress and intonation.

1 *Hi, Mr. Green. Are you busy?*

2 *No, not really. Why?*

3 *I'd like your help because I have a problem with my bike.*

4 *I can't find my glasses.*

5 *Why not?*

6 *Rachel, what does "supper" mean?*

7 *Why do you want to know?*

8 *Because Helen's mom says it.*

9 *Well, it's a different word for "dinner." Some people say it.*

6 Read the example and write a similar conversation.

Adam: Do you want to play tennis?
Roger: No, I don't. Not today.
Adam: Really? Why not?
Roger: Because I have a guitar lesson.

A: (ask a question) ____

B: (say no) ____

A: (ask why) ____

B: (give a reason) ____

63

WRITING

>>> **Write a website post**

1 Choose the correct option.

REMEMBER HOW TO …
use *and* and *but*

- Use *and* to add another (1) *similar* / *different* idea.
- Use *but* to add a (2) *different* / *similar* idea.

2 Choose the correct option.
1 I like cats, *but* / *and* I don't like dogs.
2 I eat fish, *and* / *but* I don't eat meat.
3 I often swim, *and* / *but* I can't play basketball.
4 I'm active, *but* / *and* I play a lot of sports.
5 I keep a diary, *and* / *but* I don't write stories.
6 I often meet my friends, *but* / *and* we usually go to the movies.

3 Look at the table about a hotel. Choose the correct option.

Swimming pool	Near the ocean	Restaurant	24-hour reception	Breakfast	Friendly people
✗	✓	✗	✗	✓	✓

My hotel (1) *doesn't* / *does* have a swimming pool, (2) *but* / *and* we can get to the ocean in five minutes. For lunch and dinner we usually eat in a restaurant, (3) *but* / *and* the hotel room includes a small breakfast. There (4) *is* / *isn't* a night receptionist, (5) *and* / *but* we can call at any time. The people here (6) *aren't* / *are* very friendly (7) *and* / *but* help us with ideas for where to go.

4 Complete the sentences with *and* or *but*.

What's my PERFECT VACATION?

I'm in Mexico. There's no rain, (1) *and* the weather's perfect. My hotel is great, (2) ____ it has a swimming pool and tennis courts. I swim every day, (3) ____ I don't sit next to the pool and read like my mom. That's boring! My mom and dad are here, (4) ____ my sister, Becca, too. We sometimes play tennis, (5) ____ not every day. The restaurant at the hotel is great. It has good food. I like the chocolate ice cream, (6) ____ I don't like the vanilla ice cream. At night, we go for a walk, (7) ____ we have something to drink at a café. Then we go back to the hotel, (8) ____ we play games before bedtime. I like computer games, (9) ____ I don't like board games. We only play computer games. 🙂

64

5 You're going to write a website post about a perfect school day. Imagine you can change anything you want about your own school day. Make notes. Use the *Writing plan* to help you.

WRITING PLAN

1 What time does school start and finish? ☐

2 What classes do you have? How often? ☐

3 Do you always have free school meals? What is usually for lunch? ☐

WRITE AND CHECK

6 Write your message. Write about 50 words. Then check (✓) the stages in the *Writing plan*.

>>> **Ask for help**

1 Complete the **REFLECTION POINT** with the words in the box.

family   help   ~~important~~   something   students   teacher

2 Which questions are asking for help? Check (✓) a or b.

1 a Can you play the guitar? ☐
   b Can you show me how to play the guitar? ☑
2 a Can you help me find my keys? ☐
   b Can you give me your keys? ☐
3 a Can you speak Spanish? ☐
   b Can you pronounce that Spanish sentence, please? ☐
4 a Can you show me how to do this math problem? ☐
   b Can you understand this math problem? ☐
5 a Can you restart my computer, please? ☐
   b Can you use a computer? ☐
6 a Can you help me with dinner? ☐
   b Can you cook? ☐

REFLECTION POINT

It's (1) *important* to ask for (2) _____ if you don't understand (3) _____. In class, ask the (4) _____ or other (5) _____. At home, ask your (6) _____ .

3 Complete the questions asking for help.

> I don't know where my shoes are.

1 Can you help *me find my shoes* ?

> I don't remember the homework assignment.

2 Can you tell _____ ?

> I don't know how to use this camera.

3 Can you show _____ ?

> I'm sorry, but I don't understand German.

4 Can you speak _____ ?

SCHOOL SKILLS

65

VOCABULARY REVIEW   UNITS 1-5

1 Choose the best option, a, b, or c.
1. Can I ___ your bike for an hour?
   a fetch   (b) borrow   c cross
2. What pet do you want to ___ ?
   a adopt   b order   c shake
3. I'm ___ but I can read sign language.
   a blind   b old   c deaf
4. What's a ___ school day like for you?
   a normal   b mystery   c dark
5. The first meal of the day is ___ .
   a lunch   b dinner   c breakfast
6. There's a great new ___ at the Rex Theater.
   a routine   b movie   c influence
7. What's the ___ of your book?
   a heading   b post   c title
8. I take a ___ every morning.
   a get up   b shower   c bed

2 Read the clues and write the words.
1. This is a very big animal.   E _ _ _ _ T
2. It lives in water.   F _ H
3. He's my father's son.   B _ _ _ R
4. He works in the theater.   A _ _ _ R
5. He's my dad's dad.   G _ _ _ _ A
6. You can ride it.   H _ _ E
7. She's my grandma's child.   M _ _ _ R
8. It flies in the sky.   B _ _ D
9. It's a popular pet.   R _ _ _ T
10. She works in a hospital.   D _ _ _ R
11. It isn't you; it's ___ .   M _
12. It isn't him; it's ___ .   H _

3 Find the words from Exercise 2 in the word search.

F	R	H	D	F	H	M	G	M	X
I	A	O	O	H	E	E	D	O	E
S	B	R	C	Y	R	S	O	T	R
H	B	S	T	R	S	L	C	H	A
(E	L	E	P	H	A	N	T)	E	B
M	T	H	R	A	C	T	O	R	B
G	R	A	N	D	P	A	R	X	I
B	I	R	D	Z	O	E	B	F	T
S	P	B	R	O	T	H	E	R	Z

4 Choose the word that is different from the others.
1. a drums   b guitar   (c) hip-hop
2. a piano   b rock   c pop
3. a horse   b hamster   c clock
4. a bed   b picture   c chair
5. a nose   b rabbit   c face
6. a shower   b actor   c cook
7. a nurse   b farmer   c doctor
8. a bad   b good   c terrible
9. a turtle   b sunglasses c T-shirt
10. a bike   b notebook   c car

ALL ABOUT ME

1. What job would you like to do? Why?

2. Who's your favorite famous person? Why?

3. What's your favorite animal? Why?

GRAMMAR REVIEW   UNITS 1-5

1 **Choose the correct options.**

(1) *I'm not* / *I don't* know what (2) *you think* / *do you think*, but I (3) *believe* / *believes* it's important to start the day with something active. I go for (4) *a* / *the* run three times a week with (5) *my* / *me* dad before school. We get up at 6:30 and run for half an hour. Then we (6) *have* / *has* breakfast and I get ready for school. What (7) *you do* / *do you do* to stay healthy? (8) *Are* / *Do* you play any sports?

2 **Complete the questions and answers with the words in the box.**

| 'm not   am   can   ~~can't~~   do   don't |

1 Q: Can you hear me?
   A: No, I _can't_ .
2 Q: Do you work there?
   A: Yes, I _____ .
3 Q: Are you Colombian?
   A: No, I _____ .
4 Q: Can you help me?
   A: Yes, I _____ .
5 Q: Do you know Bill?
   A: No, I _____ .
6 Q: Are you happy?
   A: Yes, I _____ .

3 **Choose the correct options from the box below.**

Kevin (1) ____ to be an actor. His mom and dad (2) ____ actors, and they often (3) ____ in different cities or countries. People (4) ____ it's a great job, but sometimes it (5) ____ difficult. They (6) ____ famous. When they finish a play, they (7) ____ always find work. They often don't have a job for months, but Kevin (8) ____ the life of an actor. He (9) ____ want a lot of money.

1	a want	b is wants	c (wants)
2	a is	b are	c be
3	a are work	b works	c work
4	a think	b do think	c thinks
5	a does	b has	c is
6	a don't	b aren't	c haven't
7	a can't to	b aren't	c can't
8	a love	b loves	c is loves
9	a doesn't	b don't	c does

4 **Complete the text. Use the words in the box.**

| can   don't   goes   ~~have~~   my   our   there |

I (1) _have_ one brother and two sisters. (2) _____ are six people in my family – my two sisters, my brother, Mom, Dad, and me. Our house isn't very big, so we (3) _____ have our own rooms. (4) _____ brother and I have a small room. My sisters have a big room. (5) _____ rooms have big windows. We (6) _____ see the beach. It's beautiful. My family (7) _____ to the beach on Sunday. That's my Mom in the picture. We're at the beach.

67

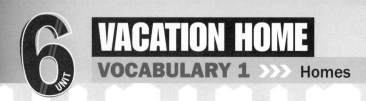

6 VACATION HOME
VOCABULARY 1 >>> Homes

1 Look at the picture. What's wrong with this room? Complete the sentences below.

1 The light is on the _bed_.
2 The clock is on the _____.
3 The chair is on the _____.
4 The bed is on the _____.
5 The door is on the _____.
6 The computer is on the _____.

2 Which of these things are inside a house? Put a check (✓) or an ✗ next to each thing.

1 apartment ✗
2 swimming pool ____
3 yard ____
4 balcony ____
5 hotel ____
6 kitchen ____
7 terrace ____
8 hall ____

3 Which of these words can you add the word "room" to? Check (✓) them.

1 hall ____
2 bed ✓
3 living ____
4 kitchen ____
5 bath ____
6 dining ____

4 Which of the rooms you checked in Exercise 3 are two words?

1 _____ 2 _____

5 Write the words for the rooms (A–F) in the picture.

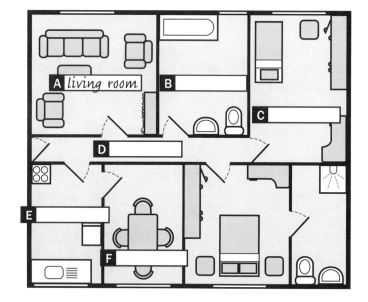

6 Complete the text with the words in the box.

> ~~apartment~~   balcony   bathroom   bedroom
> dining room   hall   kitchen

Look at our new (1) _apartment_. It has a guest (2) _____, so you can come and stay with us if you want. The (3) _____ is also the living room, so we can eat and watch TV at the same time. The (4) _____ is small, but it's OK for cooking. It has a refrigerator and a stove. There isn't a (5) _____. When you open the door, you walk into the living room. The (6) _____ has a shower and a bathtub. But the best thing is the big (7) _____. We can sit outside and relax. It's really nice.

READING

>>> Read chat messages

1 Match the pictures (1–4) to the places (a–d).

a houseboat   _3_
b house   ____
c boat   ____
d tent   ____

2 Read the chat messages. Who's living in an unusual vacation house – Jason or Anna? ____

GO BEYOND — INSTANT MESSENGER

JASON: Hi, Anna. I'm on vacation. My family has a houseboat on a lake. Here are some more pictures of the houseboat.
ANNA: Cool! What's it like?
JASON: The bedrooms are very small, but that's OK. My brother and I always go outside. We like to fish and swim.
ANNA: Is there a kitchen?
JASON: There's a small kitchen, but there isn't a dining room. We put a table and chairs outside and eat our meals.
ANNA: And is there a bathroom?
JASON: Of course! There's a special kind of toilet for the houseboat, and there's a small shower.
ANNA: Is the houseboat comfortable?
JASON: Yes, it is. It's more comfortable than a tent. I feel safer too because the houseboat has walls. This vacation is better than our camping vacation last year.

READING TIP
Look at pictures before you read. They give you information about the text.

3 Read the chat messages again. Choose the correct answer, a, b, or c.
1 Jason and his family are …
  a in a house.   b on a houseboat.   c in a tent.
2 The houseboat has …
  a small bedrooms.   b a dining room.   c no bathroom.
3 The family eats their meals …
  a in the bathroom.   b a in the kitchen.   c outside.
4 Jason thinks the houseboat is …
  a cool.   b big.   c comfortable.
5 Jason doesn't feel safe in …
  a a house.   b a tent.   c a houseboat.
6 Jason prefers …
  a the tent.   b his bedroom.   c the houseboat.

MOVE BEYOND
What kinds of houses do you know? Go on the internet and find pictures of houses in warm climates and cold climates. Make some notes and discuss different houses in your next class.

4 Check (✓) the picture that shows shows a beach vacation, a, b, or c. Put an X on the vacation place you prefer.

GRAMMAR 1 Comparative adjectives

>>> Compare two places, people, or things

1 **Complete the grammar table with the words in the box.**

better   more   noisier   ~~older~~   worse

One-syllable adjectives + -er
My dad's five years (1) _older_ than my mom.
Two-syllable adjectives with -y + -ier
A motorcycle is (2) _____ than a bike.
More + adjectives with two or more syllables
It's (3) _____ expensive to live in a city.
Irregular adjectives change in form.
(good) A computer is (4) _____ than a tablet. (bad) My dad's cooking is (5) _____ than my mom's cooking.

2 **Complete the sentences with the word in parentheses.**
  1 Our team is (good) _better_ than their team.
  2 My school is (far) _____ than a kilometer from my house.
  3 I don't like hip-hop music. It's (bad) _____ than rock.
  4 My dog is (friendly) _____ than my cat.
  5 It's her birthday. Of course she is (happy) _____ today.
  6 Brazil is (big) _____ than Nicaragua.
  7 The classroom is (noisy) _____ than the library.

3 ❯ **Choose the correct option.**
  1 It's *late* / (*later*) than you think.
  2 He's *short* / *shorter* than I am.
  3 It's *more cheap* / *cheaper* to shop online.
  4 Small stores are often *more friendlier* / *friendlier* than big ones.
  5 Walking is *slow* / *slower* than biking.
  6 It's *importanter* / *more important* to try than to win.
  7 Try to be *more nice* / *nicer*, please.
  8 He's one year *more older* / *older* than she is.

4 ❯ **Complete the conversation with the comparative form of the words in parentheses.**
  Tom: So, do we take our tent or stay in a small hotel?
  Rick: A hotel is (1) _more expensive_ (expensive), but it's (2) _____ (comfortable).
  Tom: Yes, it is. And it's (3) _____ (clean) than a tent with no shower.
  Rick: But we can swim in the ocean. I think a vacation in a tent is (4) _____ (interesting). It's (5) _____ (cheap), and it's (6) _____ (good) than a hotel. We can see stars.
  Tom: OK. Get the tent. Let's do it!

70

6

5 a ⟩⟩ Make comparisons using the words in parentheses.

1 a house / a tent (big)
A house is bigger than a tent.

2 cars / bicycles (expensive)

3 a hotel / an apartment (big)

4 speaking Japanese / writing Japanese (easy)

5 a plane / a train (fast)

6 the country / the city (quiet)

b ⟩⟩ Rewrite sentences 1–6 from Exercise 5a using the opposite comparative adjectives.

1 *A tent is smaller than a house.*
2
3
4
5
6

6 ⟩⟩⟩ Write sentences comparing each pair of pictures. Use the adjectives in the box only once.

| cheap   cold   dangerous   ~~dry~~   expensive |
| fast   hot   safe   slow   ~~wet~~ |

The Sahara desert

Greenland

The Audu

The Mono

1 *The Sahara desert is drier than Greenland.*
2 *Greenland is wetter than the Sahara desert.*
3
4

The crocodile pool

The swimming pool

7
8
9
10

5
6

71

LISTENING

>>> **Understand a conversation about food**

1 a Write the words for the food in the pictures (1–9).

1   pasta ✓

2   p _____ ☐

3   e _____ ☐

4   c _____ ☐

5   s _____ ☐

6   c _____ ☐

7   b _____ ☐

8   r _____ e ☐

9   s _____ ☐

b ▶30 Now listen and check (✓) the food you hear.

2 ▶30 Listen again. Check (✓) the things each person says he or she eats/drinks.

1

	Steak	Cheese	Pasta	Fish	Chicken
Lucia					✓

2

	Steak	Vegetables	Eggs	Fruit	Salad	Cheese
Frank						

3

	Juice	Cheese	Milk	Vegetables
Tara				

3 ▶30 Listen again. Write each person's favorite food. Choose from the words in the box. You only need three words.

carrots   cheese   chicken   eggs   pasta   steak

Person	Favorite food
Lucia	
Frank	
Tara	

4 ▶30 Listen again and decide if the statements are true (*T*) or false (*F*).

1   Lucia only eats red meat.   T/**F**
2   Frank has a lot of food in his garden.   T/F
3   Frank doesn't buy meat.   T/F
4   Tara makes Chinese food.   T/F
5   Tara eats a lot of burgers.   T/F

VOCABULARY 2

>>> **Food and drink**

1 Write the names of the fruits and match the pictures (a–f) to the names (1–6).

1 o r a n g e   c

2 b _ _ n _

3 w _ e _ m _ l _

4 a _ _ l e

5 g _ _ _ s

6 l _ _ o _

a

b

c

d

e

f

2 Read the clues and write the words.

1 It's a kind of meat. This animal makes eggs.   c h i c k e n
2 You can cook with this or put it on a salad.   o _ _
3 It can be white or brown, and you use it to make a sandwich.   b _ _ _
4 It's very popular in China.   r _ _ _

3 Choose the best option.

1 (Fish) / Chickens come from the ocean.
2 Do you want milk in your *pizza* / *coffee* ?
3 Steak is my favorite *pizza* / *meat* .
4 I always have orange *oil* / *juice* with my breakfast.
5 My mom drinks a lot of *water* / *pasta* .
6 We usually have *eggs* / *ice cream* for Sunday breakfast.

4 Choose the best option.

1 (steak)/ watermelon and fries
2 *vegetables* / *oil* and rice with chicken
3 *cheese* / *grape* and watermelon fruit salad
4 a *rice* / *cheese* and chicken sandwich
5 a *milk* / *fruit* salad

5 Choose the word that is different from the others.

1 a juice   b milk   (c) steak
2 a meat   b chicken   c tea
3 a pasta   b rice   c lemon
4 a fish   b chicken   c steak
5 a banana   b grapes   c ice cream
6 a sandwich   b hamburger c juice

6 Complete the text with the words in the box.

| juice melon salad soda ~~sweet~~ |

I love (1) _sweet_ things like chocolate, but I'm careful I don't eat a lot of them. I always eat good things like vegetables or a green (2) _____ with my lunch and dinner. I don't drink (3) _____ because there are a lot of tasty fruit (4) _____ s that are better for you. My favorite juice is made of apple, orange, and (5) _____ . I make it at home.

WORDS & BEYOND

7 Choose the correct option.

1 The Netherlands is in (Europe)/ *Latin America* .
2 Mexico is in *Latin America* / *Europe* .
3 The first *views* / *courses* at the Brazilian restaurant are very good.
4 How strange! This is a very *dirty* / *expensive* street. Most of Vancouver is beautiful and clean.
5 Washington, DC is the *capital* / *far* city of the USA.
6 I'm on vacation in Peru. Look at the great *fact* / *view* from the window!

8 Choose the correct answers.

1 Where can you put food?
   (a) in a cabinet   b in a clock   c in a kilo
2 Where's a balcony?
   a outside   b in a room   c on the floor
3 Which thing can you take with you?
   a a house   b a tent   c an apartment
4 Which food comes from Latin America?
   a Mexican   b German   c Chinese
5 Which is a positive (good) word?
   a comfortable   b dangerous   c dirty
6 Which word means that something costs a lot of money?
   a expensive   b meal   c safe
7 Which word is something you buy on vacation?
   a safe   b souvenir   c cabinet

73

GRAMMAR 2 *Some* and *any*, *much* and *many*

>>> Talk about how much there is of something

1 Complete the table with words or phrases from the box.

~~are~~   are   are a lot of   aren't any   aren't many   is (x2)   is a lot of   isn't any   many   not much

Countable	Uncountable	Countable and uncountable
There's a banana. There are bananas. There (1) _are_ apples.	There's milk. There (2) _____ rice.	There are some bananas. There's some milk. There (3) _____ some apples. There (4) _____ some rice.
There are many bananas. There are (5) _____ apples.		There are a lot of bananas. There's a lot of milk. There (6) _____ rice. There (7) _____ apples.
There aren't many bananas. There (8) _____ apples.	There's not much milk. There's (9) _____ rice.	There aren't any bananas. There isn't any milk. There (10) _____ rice. There (11) _____ apples.

2 >> Complete the table with the words in the box. Add plural forms when you need to.

banana   bread   burger   ~~cheese~~   egg   food
meat   orange   pasta   rice   sandwich

Much	Many
cheese	

3 >> Complete the sentences with *much* or *many*.

1. I don't have _much_ money.
2. Do you have _____ friends?
3. There aren't _____ cafés we can go to near here.
4. I don't have _____ homework this weekend.
5. Do you have _____ things to do on Saturday?
6. I don't have _____ time to talk now. Call you later.

4 >> Choose the correct options from the box below.

Customer: Hello. I'd like (1) ___ juice, please.
Server: OK. Do you want (2) ___ special kind of juice?
Customer: Well, do you have (3) ___ apple juice?
Server: Uh, yes … um … no, we don't. Not (4) ___ people ask for apple juice.
Customer: OK. Do you have (5) ___ mango juice?
Server: No, we don't have (6) ___ right now. I'm sorry.
Customer: All right. Well, I'm sure you have (7) ___ bottle of orange juice.
Server: Well, yes, uh … no, not today. We don't have (8) ___ juice today.
Customer: Well, do you have (9) ___ hot chocolate?
Server: Yes, we have hot chocolate.

1	a much	ⓑ some	c any
2	a any	b a lot of	c much
3	a many	b any	c a
4	a any	b much	c many
5	a an	b some	c any
6	a a lot of	b any	c many
7	a a lot of	b any	c a
8	a any	b many	c a
9	a much	b any	c a

5 >>> Complete the conversation with *much*, *many*, *some*, or *any*.

Amy: What's in the refrigerator?
Sue: There isn't (1) _much_. In fact, there aren't (2) _____ things at all.
Amy: Well, are there (3) _____ vegetables to make a salad?
Sue: There are (4) _____ tomatoes – only two or three, but they look old.
Amy: Don't worry. Is there (5) _____ pasta?
Sue: Yes, there's (6) _____ in the cabinet.
Amy: Do we have (7) _____ oil?
Sue: Yes. So we can make (8) _____ pasta with tomato sauce.

SPEAKING

Ask how much something is

1 a Complete the *Phrasebook* with the words in the box.

| are | can | ~~is~~ | please | sure | too |

b ▶31 Now listen and check your answers.

2 Put the words in order to make questions.

You — Sales clerk

1. much / How / bag? / that / is
   How much is that bag?
   — It's 30 dollars.

2. those / How / are / much / shoes?
   — They're 40 dollars.

3. these / sunglasses? / How / are / much
   — They're 10 dollars.

4. How / is / shirt? / this / much
   — It's 25 dollars.

5. the / juice? / How / much / is
   — It's three dollars.

PHRASEBOOK

Ask how much something is
How much (1) ___is___ the / this / that juice?
How much (2) _____ the / these / those grapes?

Buy or not buy something
OK. (3) _____ I have some / it / them,
(4) _____ ?
Sorry, that's (5) _____ much.
I'm not (6) _____ . Thanks.

3 You have 20 dollars. Read what the sales clerk says in Exercise 2. Buy or don't buy the thing. Complete the sentences.

1. ☹ Sorry, that's *too much* .
2. ☹ I'm not _____ .
3. ☺ OK. Can I _____ ?
4. ☹ Sorry, that's _____ .
5. ☺ OK. Can I _____ ?

4 ▶32 Listen to three conversations. What do the people want to buy?

Conversation 1 _____
Conversation 2 _____
Conversation 3 _____

5 ▶32 Who buys something – the person in Conversation 1, 2, or 3? Listen again to check.

Conversation _____

6 ▶33 Listen and repeat the sentences. Pay special attention to stress and intonation.

Conversation 1
Rick: How much are these soccer shoes?
Clerk: They're 75 dollars.
Rick: Sorry, that's too much.

Conversation 2
Liz: How much is this computer?
Clerk: It's 244 dollars.
Liz: Mmm. I'm not sure. Thanks.

Conversation 3
Ed: How much is this pen?
Clerk: It's 99 cents.
Ed: OK. Can I have it, please?

7 Write two conversations: (1) you buy something; (2) you don't buy something.

A: How _____ ?
B: It's / They're _____ .
A: OK _____ .

A: How _____ ?
B: It's / They're _____ .
A: Sorry, _____ .

WRITING

›› Write a text message

1 Choose the correct option.

REMEMBER HOW TO ...

use *too*

- Use *too* to add another (1) **different** / **similar** idea.
- Use *too* at the (2) **end** / **start** of a sentence.

2 a Read the text messages from Adam and Jane. Choose the correct options.

b Now complete Adam's next message. Put the words in *italics* in order.

A
Hi Jane, where's your hotel? I can't believe we're in the same place on vacation! What beach do you usually go to? I go to Sunshine Beach. It's better than the others. There's a great restaurant on the beach with paella and fish. Can we meet there early this afternoon? Maybe about 12:00?

B
Adam! I go to (1) *too* / – Sunshine Beach (2) *too* / – ! I love (3) *too* / – paella (4) *too* / –. I know that restaurant! I often (5) *too* / – eat there with my parents (6) *too* / –. It's a great place, and it's near my hotel (the Seaview). See you later. Oh … Mark's (7) *too* / – here (8) *too* / –. Can he come along?

C
Hey Jane! Of course (1) *can / too / Mark / come / !*
Mark can come too!
What do you want to eat? I like the paella. (2) *love / I / too / fresh fish /.*
I can't decide! Before we eat, we can play beach volleyball. (3) *can / We / too / go swimming /.*
Sound good? See you soon. ☺

3 Choose the best answer, a or b, to add a similar idea.

1 I have a great view from my hotel balcony.
   a I have a pet too.
   b There's a swimming pool here too.
2 The people here are mostly Brazilians.
   a There are some Germans too.
   b I speak German too.
3 The breakfast here is great.
   a The waiters are nice too.
   b I like the eggs too.
4 The local town is 10 minutes away by bus.
   a We ride bikes too.
   b We can go there by taxi too.
5 I usually go to bed late.
   a I get up late too.
   b I read a lot too.
6 I speak to people in English.
   a I love Spanish food too.
   b I practice my Spanish here too.

6

4 You're going to write a text message to a friend about a restaurant you are in for a family birthday. Make notes. Use the *Writing plan* to help you.

WRITING PLAN

1 Where is the restaurant? Is it near your home? ☐

....

....

2 What are the place and the food like? Does the restaurant have live music? ☐

....

....

3 How does it compare with other restaurants you know? Is it better / worse / more interesting ...? ☐

....

....

....

WRITE AND CHECK

5 Write your message. Write about 50 words. Then check (✓) the stages in the *Writing plan*.

⟫⟫⟫ Try new things

1 Choose the correct options to complete the **REFLECTION POINT**.

2 ▶34 Listen to the speakers. Match the subjects (a–d) to the people (1–4).

1 Sasha	*b*	**a**	friends
2 Nick	....	**b**	food
3 Mike	....	**c**	vacation
4 Tina	....	**d**	music

3 ▶34 Listen again. What new things do they try? Write the new thing. Write X if the speaker doesn't try a new thing.

1 Sasha   *cooking*   **3** Mike ....
2 Nick   ....   **4** Tina ....

4 ▶35 Listen again to Tina's recording. You're Tina's friend. Complete the text message to Tina on the right. Tell her some new things she can try.

5 a ▶36 Listen again to Nick's recording. Decide if the statements are true (*T*) or false (*F*).

1 Nick's vacations are exciting. T/**F**
2 Nick does the same things all the time on vacation. T/F
3 Nick meets new people on vacation. T/F

b Help Nick. What can he do? Write three things.

....

....

....

REFLECTION POINT ◀◀

It's (1) ⟨*easier*⟩ / *more difficult* (but sometimes boring) to do (2) *different / the same* things. Try (3) *new / old* things! You can learn (4) *something / nothing* new, make (5) *new / the same* friends, and have more (6) *work / fun* .

Hi Tina! You're not boring. But don't do the same things all the time. THAT'S boring. You have more to talk about when you do new things. So try new things. You can
(1) .... You can
(2) .... too. Or you can (3) .... Talk to you soon. ☺

SCHOOL SKILLS

77

VOCABULARY REVIEW

UNITS 1-6

1 Choose the correct options from the box below.

I live in a nice (1) ___ in the (2) ___ of the town. It's a(n) (3) ___ street, and there aren't many cars. All the (4) ___ are friendly. That's good! A lot of people have dogs, and I meet them when I take our dog Lexi to the park. It's a daily (5) ___ for me. I go with her before (6) ___ in the morning and again when I get (7) ___ from school.

1	(a) house	b yard	c kitchen
2	a left	b right	c middle
3	a same	b old	c quiet
4	a neighbors	b players	c turtles
5	a survey	b routine	c message
6	a dinner	b lunch	c breakfast
7	a home	b house	c apartment

2 Write the names of the animals (a–f). Then match the pictures (a–f) to the sentences (1–6).

1 *I'm small, with four legs, and you can keep me in your bedroom.* [b]

2 *I'm big, and you can ride me.* ☐

3 *I live in water.* ☐

4 *I have big, long ears.* ☐

5 *I'm a bird, and I usually live outside.* ☐

6 *I'm bigger than a mouse, and I like to play with mice.* ☐

c ___
a ___
e ___
f ___
d ___
r ___
b ___
f ___
h ___
h ___
c ___

3 Complete the text with the words or phrases in the box.

audio books   disabilities   ~~hearing aid~~   sign language   technology   wheelchair

People who are a little deaf often use a (1) *hearing aid* . They can learn to use (2) ___ too. Blind people can listen to (3) ___ , and people who can't use their legs can move with a (4) ___ . People with different (5) ___ live normal active lives. Science and (6) ___ help them a lot.

4 Match the words (a–h) to the places (1–8).

1	hospital	*e*	a cook
2	restaurant	___	b player
3	farm	___	c receptionist
4	hotel	___	d sales clerk
5	school	___	e nurse
6	soccer team	___	f animal
7	store	___	g family
8	house	___	h teacher

ALL ABOUT ME

1 What's your favorite place to eat? Why?

2 What's your favorite school subject? Why?

3 What's your favorite movie? Why?

78

GRAMMAR REVIEW   UNITS 1–6

1 Complete the sentences with the word in parentheses.
1 (interesting) It's *more interesting* to be a doctor than a farmer.
2 (famous) Actors in movies are _____ than teachers.
3 (exciting) A job in a movie is _____ than a job in a restaurant.
4 (busy) Do you think waiters are _____ than nurses?
5 (good) I think a cook is a _____ job than a waitress.

2 a Complete the questions with *Whose*, *Who is*, or *Who has*.
1 *Whose* phone is this?   *Alice's*
2 _____ your best friend?   _____
3 _____ my pen?   _____
4 _____ family has a pet?   _____
5 _____ that noisy girl?   _____
6 _____ house is that there?   _____
7 _____ a bicycle?   _____
8 _____ book is that?   _____

b Now answer the questions in Exercise 2a with *Alice* or *Alice's*.

3 a Choose the correct option.
1 She usually **play** / (**plays**) soccer on Saturdays.
2 She **likes** / **don't like** blue jeans.
3 She **isn't** / **doesn't** have long hair.
4 There **is** / **are** two boys.
5 John **wears** / **wear** glasses.
6 **They** / **There** are happy.

b Write questions for the answers (1–6) in Exercise 3a.
1 she / play / soccer?
  When *does she play soccer?*
2 clothes / she / like?
  What _____
3 she / long hair?
  Does _____
4 many / boys / there?
  How _____
5 wear / glasses?
  Who _____
6 they / happy?
  Are _____

4 Complete the text. Write one word in each blank.

| a   a lot of   Can   Do   ~~have~~   is   lot of   many   on   your |

Jackie: I (1) *have* a small problem. (2) _____ you help me?
Tara: Sure. What (3) _____ it?
Jackie: Well, it's my birthday next week.
Tara: Yes. It's (4) _____ Saturday. And there's a party at (5) _____ house.
Jackie: That's the problem. I can't invite (6) _____ people. My house isn't very big, and we don't have (7) _____ space for dancing. (8) _____ you think it's better to have (9) _____ beach party at Sunset Beach?
Tara: Yes. That's a great idea. Then a (10) _____ people can come.

UNIT 7 THEATER WORKSHOP

VOCABULARY 1 >>> Clothes

1 **Complete the colors with *a, e, i, o,* or *u*.**

1 wh _i_ t e
2 p _ _ nk
3 _ _ r _ _ ng
4 y _ _ ll _ _ w
5 bl _ _ ck
6 p _ _ rpl _ _
7 bl _ _ _ _
8 gr _ _ _ _ n
9 br _ _ wn
10 r _ _ d

2 **Answer the quiz.**

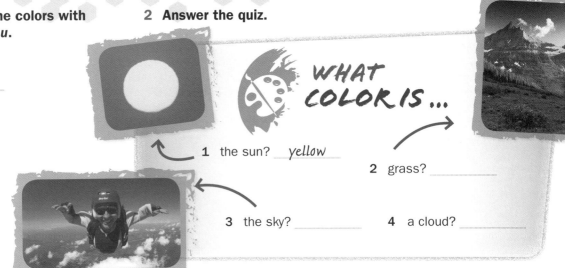

WHAT COLOR IS...

1 the sun? _yellow_
2 grass? _____
3 the sky? _____
4 a cloud? _____

3 **Find nine clothes and accessories words in the word search. Then match the pictures (a–i) to the words (1–9).**

T	K	L	S	T	L	T	L	J
P	A	C	R	S	E	E	H	E
A	W	I	E	K	H	N	A	A
N	H	J	C	Y	S	O	T	N
T	F	A	Y	U	O	Q	E	S
S	J	S	H	I	R	T	N	S
R	B	A	C	K	P	A	C	K
S	K	I	R	T	S	M	J	O
S	O	C	K	S	D	T	Q	Y

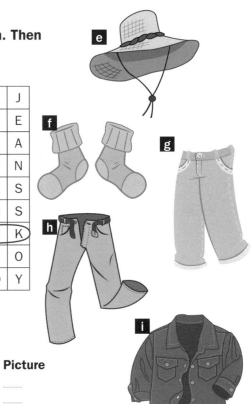

	Word	Picture		Word	Picture
1	B A C K P A C K	a	6	S O _ _ _ _	_____
2	H _ _	_____	7	P _ _ _ _ S	_____
3	S _ _ _ _	_____	8	S _ _ _ _ S	_____
4	SK _ _ _	_____	9	J _ _ _ _ _	_____
5	J _ _ _ _	_____			

4 **Find any four clothes or accessories words in the word snake.**

1 _dress_   2 _____   3 _____   4 _____

5 **Decide which things people usually wear on the top half of their body (T) or the bottom half of their body (B).**

1 jeans _B_
2 pants _____
3 skirt _____
4 hat _____
5 T-shirt _____
6 sweatshirt _____
7 socks _____
8 jacket _____

READING

Read part of a play

READING TIP ✓

You don't need to understand every word. Use the words that you know to help you.

1 Read the play quickly and answer the questions.
1 How many people are in the scene? _three_
2 Where are the people in the scene? _____

2 🔊37 **Now read and listen to the play.**

Scene One: In the garden of the castle

King: Princess Aurelia!
Princess: [entering] Yes, Father?
King: My daughter, you are a young woman now. It's time for you to find a prince to marry. Now I have …
Princess: But Father, I … I'm not looking for a husband.
King: No, you aren't, but I am looking for a husband for you. Now I have a prince. He's coming today. He's rich and intelligent …
Princess: Please, Father. I … I … I don't want to meet the prince. I know the man I want to marry. He comes here often, and we meet in the garden. We sit under the tree and talk.
King: What?! You're secretly meeting an ordinary man? I have a prince waiting for you!
Princess: But he's a good man, Father. He has a good heart. I … I … I love him. Look! He's coming now.

Prince Eric enters.

Princess: This is the man who visits me in the garden. His name is Eric.
King: *Prince* Eric, you mean! Daughter, this is the man I want you to marry.
Princess: *Prince* Eric?
Prince: Yes, *Prince* Eric. Please, Aurelia. I want you to love me because I have a good heart and not because I am a prince.
Princess: Father, this is the man I love.
King: Then I give you Prince Eric as your husband and I give you both my kingdom.

3 Complete the sentences with the correct form of the words in gray from the play.
1 My _daughter_ is my child – a girl, not a boy.
2 You _____ someone because you love them and want to have children.
3 The UK means the United _____ . It's a country that has a king or a queen.
4 Your _____ is inside your body. The word means *love and feelings* too.
5 A _____ is a place next to a house. It has trees and flowers.
6 A _____ is the man a woman is married to.

4 Choose the correct option.
1 The king **wants / doesn't want** his daughter to marry.
2 Aurelia wants to marry a man with **a lot of money / a good heart**.
3 The king is unhappy because his daughter **is secretly meeting a man / doesn't want the kingdom**.
4 The king gives his kingdom to **his daughter / his daughter and Prince Eric**.

5 Complete the text with the correct form of the words in the box.

| daughter | ~~garden~~ | heart | husband | kingdom | marry |

One day, Beauty's father goes into a castle. He eats and sleeps there. In the morning, he takes a rose from the (1) _garden_ . The Beast is living in the castle. He sees Beauty's father take the rose. He's not happy. He asks the father for his (2) _____ , Beauty. Beauty goes to the castle and lives with the Beast. He's very nice to her. He has a very good (3) _____ . He loves her, but she doesn't love him. He wants to (4) _____ her, but she doesn't want a (5) _____ . Beauty goes home to her father. One night, she has a dream – the Beast wants her to see her. Beauty goes to the castle. She knows the Beast has a good heart, and she tells him, "I love you." He changes into a prince. Beauty and the Beast marry and live in his (6) _____ .

MOVE BEYOND

Use the internet to find some pictures of actors in a play. Imagine what the actors are saying. Tell the class in your next lesson.

81

GRAMMAR 1 Present progressive

>>> Talk about things happening now

1 Complete the grammar table with the phrases in the box.

> right now   ~~She's watching TV.~~
> We aren't going out today.
> We're sitting in the living room.

Present progressive
Affirmative: *be* + verb + *-ing*
I'm doing my homework.   (1) *She's watching TV.*   (2) _____
Negative: *be* + *not* + verb + *-ing*
I'm not watching TV now.   She isn't doing her homework right now.   (3) _____
Spelling changes
(ride) Joe's riding his bike to school.   (sit) The students are sitting in class.
Time expressions
I'm leaving now.   I'm studying (4) _____ .   I'm going to school today.

2 Put the verbs in parentheses in the correct form to make present progressive sentences.

1 I (leave) school now.
   I'm leaving school now.
2 Ben (watch) a movie.
3 My internet (not work) today.
4 Sandra (sit) next to David.
5 I (not feel) very well right now.
6 We (go) into the castle now.
7 You (wear) a nice hat.
8 I (have) a great time at the party.

3 Choose the correct options to complete the chat messages.

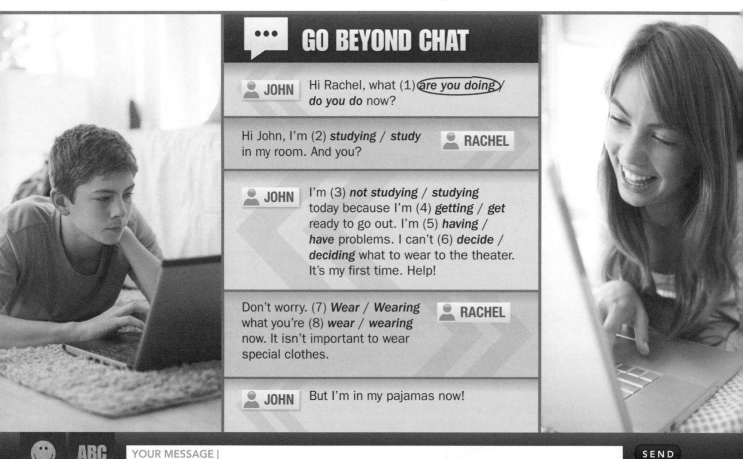

GO BEYOND CHAT

JOHN: Hi Rachel, what (1) *are you doing* / *do you do* now?

RACHEL: Hi John, I'm (2) *studying* / *study* in my room. And you?

JOHN: I'm (3) *not studying* / *studying* today because I'm (4) *getting* / *get* ready to go out. I'm (5) *having* / *have* problems. I can't (6) *decide* / *deciding* what to wear to the theater. It's my first time. Help!

RACHEL: Don't worry. (7) *Wear* / *Wearing* what you're (8) *wear* / *wearing* now. It isn't important to wear special clothes.

JOHN: But I'm in my pajamas now!

4 ›› **Put the words in order to make sentences. Use contractions of the verb *be*.**
1 is / smiling. / Jill
   Jill's smiling.
2 today. / You / staying home / are
3 to school. / are / You / not going
4 party. / are / enjoying / We / the
5 Matt / newspaper. / the / is / reading
6 driving / mother / is / My / right now.
7 swimming / in the pool. / are / They / not
8 me. / He / waiting / is / for

5 ›› **Write affirmative (+) and negative (−) sentences in the present progressive form.**
1 We (go) to the movies now
   + *We're going to the movies now.*
   − *We aren't going to the movies now.*
2 He (eat) lunch
   +
   −
3 She (cry)
   +
   −
4 We (play) computer games
   +
   −
5 They (listen) to music
   +
   −

6 ›› **Complete the status updates.**

1 ☺ *I'm swimming at the pool.*

LAURA
☺ swim at the pool

2

PATRICK
☺ ☺ play soccer at school

3

AMY AND PHILLIP
☺ ☺ walk in the park

4

VANESSA AND YUNA
☹ study for a test

5

MARK
☺ ☺ have lunch at home

LISTENING

⟫⟫ Listen to descriptions

1 ▶38 **Listen and match the places (a–f) to the sounds (1–6).**

Sounds   Places

1   *d*

2 ....

3 ....

4 ....

5 ....

6 ....

2 ▶39 **Listen and match the places (a–f) from Exercise 1 to the speakers.**

Speaker 1	*f*	Speaker 3	....	Speaker 5	....
Speaker 2	....	Speaker 4	....	Speaker 6	....

3 ▶39 **Listen again. Match the verbs you hear (a–f) to the conversations (1–6).**

Speaker 1	*c*	a	dance / enjoy
Speaker 2	....	b	carry / give
Speaker 3	....	c	point / fly
Speaker 4	....	d	drive / go
Speaker 5	....	e	eat / sit
Speaker 6	....	f	shop / wait

4 **Complete the sentences about the pictures (a–f) from Exercise 1. Use the words in the box. Listen again if you need help.**

> carry   dance   drive   ~~eat~~   enjoy   fly
> give   go   point   shop   ~~sit~~   wait

Picture a: We *'re eating* in a new restaurant. We *'re sitting* by the window.
Picture b: He _____ a puppy, and now he _____ it some food.
Picture c: The actors _____, and the people _____ the performance.
Picture d: I _____, so I can't talk. I _____ to work.
Picture e: I _____ in the store, and I _____ to pay now.
Picture f: I _____ to the bird. Look! Now it _____ away.

84

VOCABULARY 2

>>> Action verbs

1 **Complete the table with the action verbs in the box.**

carry   dance   eat   read   ride   ~~run~~   shop

Things you usually do …	
standing up	sitting down
run	

2 **Write the -ing forms for the action verbs.**
1 ride — riding
2 wait — ___
3 run — ___
4 sit — ___
5 swim — ___
6 dance — ___
7 talk — ___
8 shop — ___

3 **Look at the pictures and complete the text below with the verbs in the box. Use the present progressive form.**

carry   dance   fly   point   ride
run   shop   ~~swim~~   talk   wait

I'm looking at my friends' status updates. Look at Lara's picture: her dog (1) *is swimming* at the beach. Cool! And what about Tom's: he (2) ___ his new bike. Danny looks bored! He (3) ___ for the bus. Little Andrea (4) ___ at something, but I can't see what it is. Ellie (5) ___ . She loves dance classes. Ah! My sisters! Martina and Fiona (6) ___ as usual! And, as usual, they (7) ___ a lot of shopping bags. Pepe (8) ___ . He's very fit and healthy. He exercises all the time. Nora (9) ___ to someone on the phone. She's always on the phone! Oh, look at Michael. That's sweet: He (10) ___ a kite with his little brother.

WORDS & BEYOND

4 **Complete the text with the words in the box.**

castle   guards   king   ~~play~~
prince   queen   scene

I love the drama club. We're doing a (1) *play* about a (2) ___ who wants to be the (3) ___ . His mother is the (4) ___ . She's old, but she doesn't want to leave. There's a (5) ___ where the (6) ___ stop the prince and his men at the (7) ___ doors.

GRAMMAR 2 Present progressive

>>> **Ask and answer questions about things happening now**

1 Complete the grammar table with the words in the box.

> am Are aren't ~~Is~~ isn't ~~What~~ Where Why

Present progressive questions and answers
Yes/no questions
Are you working?
(1) _____*Is*_____ he staying with you?
(2) _____ they taking the bus?
Short answers
Yes, I (3) _____ . / No, I'm not.
Yes, she is. / No, she (4) _____ .
Yes, they are. / No, they (5) _____ .
Information questions
(6) ___*What*___ are you eating?
(7) _____ are you leaving?
(8) _____ are you going?

Hello! Good boy! Good boy!

2) Match the answers (a–g) to the questions (1–7).

1 Is the parrot talking to me?   *c*
2 Is he really speaking English?   _____
3 Are we going the right way?   _____
4 Is she calling her friend?   _____
5 Are they waiting for the bus?   _____
6 Are you studying with Jane?   _____
7 Am I helping you tonight?   _____

a No, we aren't.
b Yes, they are.
c Yes, it is.
d Yes, you are.
e No, I'm not.
f Yes, he is.
g No, she isn't.

3)) Write short answers to the questions (☹ = no ☺ = yes).

1 Are you shopping at the mall?
   ☺ *Yes, I am.*
2 Are your mom and your brother shopping with you?
   ☺ _____
3 Are you looking for shoes?
   ☹ _____
4 Are you buying hats?
   ☺ _____
5 Are you waiting to pay?
   ☹ _____

4))) Write questions in the present progressive. Use *Who, Where, What,* or *Why* at the beginning.

1 you / stay?
   Where are you staying?
2 he / do?

3 they / watch?

4 you / talk to?

5 we / do / this?

6 I / wear / this?

7 you / go?

8 she / look / at us?

5))) Complete the conversation with the correct form of the words in parentheses or short answers.

Uma: Where are you? What (1) *are you doing* (do)?
Jen: I (2) _____ (walk) to the movie theater. There are a lot of people on the street.
Uma: I (3) _____ (stand) near the café outside the movie theater. (4) _____ (come) now?
Jen: Yes, (5) _____ . I can see you. Who (6) _____ (talk) to?
Uma: That's my brother.
Jen: Your brother? Are your parents (7) _____ (come) too?
Uma: Yes, (8) _____ .
Jen: Great!

SPEAKING

7

>>> **Talk about things you like**

1 Choose the correct option.
1. I love *listen* / *listening* to music.
2. I don't like *rap music* / *listening* .
3. Do you like *act* / *acting* ?
4. *You do* / *Do you* like hip-hop?
5. I *like really* / *really like* soccer.
6. I *hate* / *hating* the color pink.

2 a Complete the *Phrasebook* with *like*, *love*, or *don't like*.

   b ▶40 **Now listen and check.**

3 ▶41 **Listen to the people talking about theater. Check (✓) the people who like theater.**

  1 Lewis ✓   2 Tess ☐   3 Emilio ☐   4 Zoe ☐

4 <u>Underline</u> the words that helped you find the answers in Exercise 3.

Lewis: I go to the theater a lot. I think the theater is <u>amazing</u>. I definitely want to be an actor.

Tess: I'm in the school play, but it's really boring. It's a 17th-century play. I don't understand it.

Emilio: For me, it's fantastic. I'm learning new things every day. The theater is a magical place.

Zoe: It's about telling stories. The story happens in front of your eyes. It's about people's lives, and it's really interesting.

5 ▶42 **Listen to the conversations. Complete the sentences.**

Conversation 1
Mr. Sims: Do you like musical (1) *theater* ?
Lewis: I love (2) _____ other people sing, but I hate (3) _____ .

Conversation 2
Mr. Sims: Do you like (4) _____ ?
Tess: I don't like (5) _____ , but I like (6) _____ .

Conversation 3
Mr. Sims: Do you like being in a play?
Emilio: Yes, I love (7) _____ .

Conversation 4
Mr. Sims: Do you like drama?
Zoe: Yes, I really (8) _____ .

6 ▶43 **Listen and repeat the sentences. Pay special attention to stress and intonation.**

Do you like going to the movies?

I love going to the movies, but I hate watching TV.

Do you like playing sports?

I don't like playing team sports, but I like playing sports on my own.

I love listening to music.

I really like it.

7 Write two conversations. Ask and answer questions about writing stories.

A: Do you like _____ ?
B: I ☺ _____ because _____ .
B: I ☹ _____ because _____ .

PHRASEBOOK

Say you like something
I (really) like / (1) _____ music / dancing.

Say you don't like something
I (2) _____ / hate dancing.

Questions
Do you (3) _____ it / music / dancing?

87

WRITING

>>> **Write a short message**

1 Choose the correct option.

REMEMBER HOW TO …

use *also*

- Use *also* to add another (1) **similar** / **different** idea.
- Use *also* (2) **before** / **after** *be*.
- Use *also* (3) **before** / **after** other verbs.

2 Check (✓) the correct second sentences. Rewrite the incorrect second sentences.

1 Uncle Joe's in Rio. Also Uncle Sam's there.
   Uncle Sam's also there.
2 He has a job there. He has a girlfriend also.

3 He loves the beach. He also likes the music.

4 He works hard. He plays also soccer.

5 His apartment has a great view. It has an also swimming pool.

6 He has a fast car. He also has a bike.

3 Match sentences a–f to sentences 1–6.

1 I'm reading a book.   c
2 The train's late.
3 I'm drinking a soda.
4 I have a new bag.
5 It's my first time in Buenos Aires.
6 I love the food here.

a It's also my first time in Argentina.
b I also have new shoes.
c I'm also listening to music.
d It's also full of people.
e I'm also eating a sandwich.
f I also like the people.

4 Check (✓) the correct text message.

A

So, here I am in downtown Athens. The people are really friendly, and they speak also English. I like walking downtown. I love sitting also in a café and watching the people. I have a cold drink, and I'm looking at the also view. It's amazing!

B

So, here I am in downtown Athens. The people are really friendly, and they also speak English. I like walking downtown. I also love sitting in a café and watching the people. I have a cold drink, and I'm also looking at the view. It's amazing!

7

5 You're going to write a text message to a friend. You're on a bus. You're going somewhere fun. Make notes. Use the *Writing plan* to help you.

WRITING PLAN

1 Where are you going? Who is with you? ☐

2 What do you like or not like about the bus? ☐

3 What two things do you like about the place you are going? ☐

WRITE AND CHECK

6 Write your message. Write about 50 words. Then check (✓) the stages in the *Writing plan*.

⟩⟩⟩ Be polite

1 Read the **REFLECTION POINT**. Who is being polite? Check (✓) a or b.

1
  a Hey, you! Come here. ☐
      b Can you please come here, George? ☑

2
  a What time is it? ☐
      b Excuse me. Can you tell me the time? ☐

3
  a I'm very sorry; I can't come to your party. ☐
      b I don't want to come to your party, OK? ☐

4
  a Thank you for your present. ☐
      b Put my present over there. ☐

> **REFLECTION POINT** ⟨⟨
> It's important to be polite when you speak and ask for things. Always think of other people and help them.

2 Choose the best options.

(1) *Thank you* / *I'm sorry* for choosing our restaurant. (2) *Excuse me* / *Please* come again.

(3) *Please* / *Thank you* ask any questions now.
(4) *I'm sorry* / *Please*, but you can't talk in the test.

(5) *Sorry* / *Excuse me* , we're closed today.
(6) *Thank you* / *Excuse me* for shopping with us.
(7) *Sorry* / *Please* come back on Wednesday.

(8) *Excuse me* / *Thank you* . Can you tell me where the bus station is?

3 Read the situations. What do you do to be polite? Check (✓) the best option, a or b.

1 The school bell rings at the end of the class.
  a You stand up and leave the classroom. ☐
  b You wait for the teacher to say you can go. ☑
2 Somebody comes to your house to help you with your new computer.
  a You ask if the person wants a glass of water or some soda. ☐
  b You tell them to work fast because you have soccer practice. ☐
3 You're sitting in the movies. Your phone starts ringing.
  a You answer it. ☐
  b You turn it off. ☐
4 You're waiting to pay for a lot of things in a supermarket. A woman asks if she can go first and pay for a bottle of water.
  a You say "yes." ☐
  b You say "no." ☐

SCHOOL SKILLS

89

VOCABULARY REVIEW

UNITS 1–7

1 Put the words in the box into the correct categories.

apartment balcony brother cheese classmate
hat jacket meat rice socks waiter yard

Food	Clothes	Places	People
		balcony	

2 Match a–g to 1–7 to make phrases.

1 mountain _a_   a bike
2 fruit   _____   b clerk
3 South   _____   c America
4 text   _____   d hands
5 shake   _____   e game
6 video   _____   f message
7 sales   _____   g salad

3 Complete the text with *have*, *go*, or *do*.

I always (1) _have_ a good breakfast before I (2) _____ to school. I (3) _____ my homework after school. I (4) _____ to my piano lesson every Tuesday and Thursday. I like to (5) _____ to the movies on Saturdays. I usually (6) _____ lunch at my grandparents' house on Sundays. I (7) _____ to bed early on Sunday nights.

4 Complete the text with the words in the box.

arm basketball drums (x2) hamster horse house Latin (x2)

I love animals. I have a pet (1) _hamster_ at home. My uncle has a (2) _____ farm, and I often go there. He has a broken (3) _____ right now, so I help him on the farm almost every day. I'm not on the farm today. No ... today I'm playing (4) _____ with my dad. He plays it a lot. It looks easy, but it isn't – trust me! I'm better at playing the (5) _____ . I love music. My favorite kind is (6) _____ . Most of my friends at school live in apartments, but I'm lucky because I live in a big (7) _____ in the country. That means I can play the (8) _____ and listen to loud (9) _____ music any time I want. ☺

ALL ABOUT ME

1 What three things do you usually do on Mondays?

2 What three things do you usually do on weekends?

90

GRAMMAR REVIEW

UNITS 1-7

1 Choose the correct options.

I'm happy that I'm (1) **work** / **working** with you today in this theater workshop. We're (2) **trying** / **can try** to understand the play. Why (3) **doesn't** / **isn't** the queen want the Black Prince to come to the castle? She's (4) **him** / **his** mother, and she tells (5) **him** / **her** husband that this isn't good news. (6) **Are** / **Do** you think that their son (7) **wants** / **is wanting** to be king?

2 Choose the correct options from the box below.

Dale: There isn't (1) ___ time. The taxi's (2) ___. I (3) ___ see it from the window. (4) ___ on! (5) ___ are you always late?
Jay: (6) ___ it! I'm ready. Let's go. How (7) ___ money do we have with us?
Dale: We have more (8) ___ we need.

1	a many	b much	c lot
2	a waiting	b wait	c to wait
3	a can	b do	c am
4	a Come	b Coming	c Comes
5	a What	b Why	c Who
6	a Stop	b Stopping	c Stops
7	a many	b lot of	c much
8	a than	b of	c that

3 Complete the interview with the correct words in the box.

aren't do doesn't don't is swim swims ~~tell~~

Interviewer: Can you (1) _tell_ me about your sport? Why do you love swimming?
Mark: I love it because I can (2) ___ on my own. I (3) ___ need a team.
Interviewer: Do you like that?
Mark: Yes, I do. Sometimes my coach (4) ___ with me.
Interviewer: Who is your coach?
Mark: My dad (5) ___ my coach.
Interviewer: (6) ___ you like having your dad as your coach?
Mark: Yes, I do, but he (7) ___. He thinks I need a new coach! But there (8) ___ many good coaches out there, and I think my dad is the best of all. He just doesn't know it!

4 a Complete the questions with the words in the box.

are can ~~do~~ does doing is

1 _Do_ you have any brothers or sisters?
2 ___ you meet me after school today?
3 ___ there an airport near where you live?
4 ___ your teacher give you much homework every night?
5 ___ you 13 years old?
6 Are you ___ your homework right now?

b Now answer the questions in Exercise 4a for you with <u>short</u> answers.

1 ___   4 ___
2 ___   5 ___
3 ___   6 ___

UNIT 8 WEATHER REPORT

VOCABULARY 1 >>> Countries, the weather

1 Write the names of the six countries. Then find them in the word search.

1 B R A Z I L
2 I _ _ _ Y
3 M _ _ _ _ O
4 R _ _ _ _ A
5 C _ _ _ _ E
6 J _ _ _ _ N

R	I	L	S	H	N	O	E	A
H	A	F	E	I	D	A	I	L
B	R	A	Z	I	L	S	A	J
C	I	E	F	S	S	I	U	A
J	H	A	T	U	R	T	D	P
T	A	I	R	W	E	A	T	A
A	O	P	L	F	H	L	M	N
E	T	A	A	E	R	Y	H	N
M	E	X	I	C	O	R	F	A

2 Answer the questions about the countries in Exercise 1.
1 Which country is in Europe and Asia? Russia
2 Which country is only in Europe? _____
3 Which two countries are in South America? _____ and _____
4 Which country is only in Asia? _____

3 Match the continents (a–e) to the countries (1–5).
1 South Africa   a
2 the USA   ____
3 Germany   ____
4 Turkey   ____
5 Argentina   ____

a Africa
b Europe
c North America
d Europe and Asia
e South America

4 a Choose the correct options.

It's a good day for the beach here in Rio – another (1) **hot** / **cold** day. It's eight o'clock in the morning, and it's (2) **30** / **zero** degrees.

Now, the weather. Get ready for a wet and (3) **warm** / **windy** day in London. The temperature's 10 degrees right now. Take a jacket and an umbrella if you go out.

It's (4) **cool** / **warm** in New York, but it's nice and dry and (5) **sunny** / **raining** with a temperature of 11 degrees.

Good morning from Moscow. It isn't snowing now, but it's cloudy and (6) **warm** / **cold** with temperatures around zero.

It's a (7) **foggy** / **sunny** start to the day in Lima. Be careful if you're driving. You can't see more than 10 meters in front of you!

b ▶44 Listen and check your answers.

5 Check (✓) the types of weather that can be dangerous for drivers.
1 foggy ✓
2 raining ☐
3 sunny ☐
4 windy ☐
5 cloudy ☐
6 snowing ☐

6 Match the words (a–g) to their opposites (1–7).
1 sunny   e
2 winter   ____
3 fall   ____
4 dry season   ____
5 dry   ____
6 hot   ____
7 cool   ____

a warm
b wet
c rainy season
d cold
e cloudy
f spring
g summer

92

READING

>>> Read and take a test

1 Read the test and answer the questions.

HOW DO YOU LIKE TO LEARN?

Part A: In class

1 I usually prefer …
   a classes where I can talk about things.
   b classes where I can look at things.
   c classes where I can do things.
2 When I learn something new, I like to …
   a listen to someone and follow instructions.
   b watch someone do it.
   c learn it by doing it.

Part B: Free time

3 When I have to wait, I often …
   a sing softly.
   b draw little pictures.
   c play with things like pens in my hands.
4 When I'm on a long car trip, I usually …
   a listen to music or talk to other people in the car.
   b look out the window at the things around you.
   c want to stop, get out of the car, and walk.
5 In my free time, I prefer to …
   a listen to music.
   b watch TV.
   c go outside and play.

2 Calculate your score. Check your answers in the table below.

Mostly A answers	You're an AUDITORY learner: you learn best when you hear things, for example, the teacher talking.
Mostly B answers	You're a VISUAL learner: you learn best when you see things, for example, pictures, cartoons, and videos.
Mostly C answers	You're a KINESTHETIC learner: you like to learn by doing things.

Remember: people can be more than one kind of learner. It's OK to like watching things and doing things to learn too, for example!

3 Match the kind of learner (a, b, or c) to each activity (1–6).
   1 Read a story out loud. _a_
   2 Read a comic book and look at the pictures. ......
   3 Listen to a story on the radio. ......
   4 Look at the teacher's pictures on the board. ......
   5 Act in the play you're studying at school. ......
   6 Stop studying every 30 minutes to walk around. ......

   a auditory
   b visual
   c kinesthetic

4 a **Take this test.**

Find the Difference
There are four fish, a, b, c, and d. Which one is different? ......

b **What kind of test is this?**
   1 auditory ☐
   2 visual ☐
   3 kinesthetic ☐

MOVE BEYOND

Use the internet to find out more about the kind of learner you are. Take some notes about it. Report what you learned in your next class.

GRAMMAR 1 Was/were

>>> Describe things in the past

1 **Complete the grammar table with the words in the box.**

was (x2)   wasn't (x2)   were   weren't

Was/were
Affirmative and negative
I/He/She/it + was / (1) _wasn't_ at the beach.   We/You/They + were/weren't at the beach.
Questions and short answers
(2) _____ he/she/it at the beach?   Yes, she was. / No, she (3) _____ .   Were we/you/they at the beach?   Yes, they (4) _____ . No, they (5) _____ .
Time expressions
yesterday, on weekends, on Saturday, last Sunday / last weekend / last week   I (6) _____ there yesterday.

2 > **Choose the correct option.**

Last Sunday …
1 I *were* / *was* at the beach.
2 I *were* / *was* with my friends.
3 We *were* / *was* in the ocean for hours.
4 There *was* / *were* a lot of little fish in the water.
5 Then there *were* / *was* a big fish.
6 It *was* / *were* near us.
7 We *weren't* / *wasn't* happy.
8 It *weren't* / *wasn't* real.

3 > **Match the the answers (a–h) to the questions (1–8).**

1 Were you at the beach too? (✗) _d_
2 Was it a hot day? (✗)
3 Were you at home? (✓)
4 Were your friends with you? (✓)
5 Were your parents there? (✗)
6 Was John there? (✗)
7 Was there any food? (✓)
8 Was it good? (✓)

a No, it wasn't.
b Yes, it was.
c No, he wasn't.
d No, I wasn't.
e Yes, they were.
f No, they weren't.
g Yes, there was.
h Yes, I was.

4 > **Complete the conversations with *was*, *wasn't*, *were*, or *weren't*.**

Kara: Where (1) _were_ you? Now we're late for the movie.
Adele: Sorry, there (2) _____ any buses.
Matt: Who (3) _____ that?
Don: That (4) _____ Jim. We (5) _____ at the same school last year.
Vic: Why (6) _____ Arturo at school yesterday?
Ursula: He (7) _____ well. He (8) _____ at the doctor's office.
Sara: Who (9) _____ your best friends at your first school?
Eva: They (10) _____ Jo and Jim.

5 ›› **Complete the text with the correct past forms of the verb *be*.**

When I (1) _was_ your age (✓), there (2) _____ internet (✗), and there (3) _____ any cell phones (✗). There (4) _____ a lot of music stores, (✓) and there (5) _____ a video store (✓) on my street. That (6) _____ a long time ago (✓). You (7) _____ born then (✗).

6 ›› **Put the words in order to make sentences.**

1 you / Where / were / night? / last
   Where were you last night?
2 Were / Joe? / you / with
   ....
3 weren't / We / at home.
   ....
4 were / at the movies. / We
   ....
5 the movie / was / What / like?
   ....
6 wasn't / very / good. / It
   ....

7 ››› **Check (✓) the correct questions. Put an ✗ next to the incorrect questions and rewrite them. Then write short answers.**

1 Were it a good vacation?   ☒   *Was it a good vacation?*
2 (✓) *Yes, it was.*
3 Was you at the beach?   ☐   ....
4 (✗) .... I was in the mountains.
5 Were your mom and dad there?   ☐   ....
6 (✓) ....
7 Were your brother there too?   ☐   ....
8 (✗) ....

8 **Put the words in order to make a conversation.**

Dan: in the mountains? / it / cold / Was
   1 *Was it cold in the mountains?*
Greg: No, / warm and sunny. / was / it
   2 ....
Dan: in the mountains? / many people / there / Were
   3 ....
Greg: weren't. / No, / there
   4 ....
Dan: your grandparents / in the mountains / Were / too?
   5 ....
Greg were / Yes, / they.
   6 ....
Dan: it / a fun vacation? / Was
   7 ....
Greg: Yes, / it / the best vacation ever! / was
   8 ....

LISTENING

>>> Listen to a description of a day

1 **Check (✓) the best listening tip.**
   1 Try to understand everything first. Then listen for the general idea. ☐
   2 Listen first for the general idea. Don't try to understand everything. ☐

2 ▶45 **Listen to the conversation. What was the problem? Choose the correct option, a, b, c, or d.**
   a the weather   c the river
   b the time   d the shoes

3 ▶45 **Listen again. Decide whether the statements are true (T) or false (F).**
   1 The beginning of the day was better than the end. (T)/F
   2 Harry had lunch, and then went swimming.   T/F
   3 Harry was in the water with his sneakers.   T/F
   4 Other people helped Harry.   T/F
   5 Harry has his sneakers now.   T/F

4 **Choose the correct option, a or b.**
   1 In Exercise 2, you listen …
      a for the general idea.
      b to try to understand everything.
   2 In Exercise 3, you listen …
      a for the general idea.
      b for pieces of information.

5 **Where do you think Harry's shoes are? Choose 1, 2, or 3. Discuss your ideas in your next class. (There's no right answer.)**
   1 They're in his bag.
   2 An animal has them.
   3 They're in the river.

6 ▶46 **Listen to this conversation. What's the general idea?**
   1 Pam's vacation was great.
   2 Pam's vacation was terrible.
   3 Pam's vacation was good at first, but then it was very bad.

7 ▶46 **Now listen again. What did Pam and her family do at the beginning when it was very windy?**
   1 They went back to the beach.
   2 They did nothing.
   3 They called for help.

96

VOCABULARY 2

>>> The country

1 Choose the correct option.
1. A village is *bigger* / *(smaller)* than a town.
2. A forest is *bigger* / *smaller* than a tree.
3. *Islands* / *Mountains* often have beaches.
4. You can swim in oceans and *forests* / *rivers*.
5. The *sky* / *ocean* is cloudy today.
6. Do you like walking in the *mountains* / *sky*?

2 Complete the text with the words in the box.

beach   island   mountains   ocean   sky   town   ~~village~~

9:30

Hi April,
I live in a small (1) _village_ in the country. Our house is in the (2) _____ next to a lake. Most people work in the (3) _____ near our village. In the summer I usually go to a(n) (4) _____ for two weeks. We swim in the (5) _____ and play games on the (6) _____ . It's often cloudy and raining where I live, so I love the sun and the blue (7) _____ when I'm on vacation.
Tell me about you! 😊
Javier

WORDS & BEYOND

3 Complete the sentences with the words in the box.

~~audience~~   count   memory   picnic
seasons   snowing   sunny

1. I wasn't in the play, but I was in the _audience_ .
2. Please _____ your correct answers.
3. I can't remember. I have a really bad _____ .
4. Do you have four different _____ in your country?
5. It's a(n) _____ day.
6. We can't have our _____ because it's raining.
7. I like mountains in the winter when it is _____ .

4 a Match the descriptions (a–d) to the seasons (1–4).

In the USA …
1. spring   _b_   a It's often hot, and we go to the beach.
2. summer _____   b Trees start to be green again and flowers grow.
3. fall   _____   c It's cold, and we sometimes have snow.
4. winter _____   d We start school again after summer vacation. All the leaves fall off the trees.

b Now match the USA seasons (1–4) in Exercise 4a to the pictures (a–d).

fall

_____

_____

_____

GRAMMAR 2 Simple past

>>> Talk about events in the past

1 Complete the grammar table with the correct past forms of the verbs.

Simple past	
Regular verbs	
verb + -ed, -ied, or -d I/He/She/It/We/You/They started	
Verb	Past form
rain	(1) _____
hate	(2) _____
stop	(3) _____
try	(4) _____
Irregular verbs	
Verb	Past form
buy	(5) _____
come	(6) _____
see	(7) _____
have	(8) _____

2 » Complete the sentences with the simple past form of the regular verbs in parentheses.

I (1) _tried_ (try), and
I (2) _____ (succeed).

He (3) _____ (stop) for the night, and he (4) _____ (stay) in a hotel.

We (5) _____ (travel) to Miami, and we (6) _____ (study) there.

They (7) _____ (look) at my pictures, and they (8) _____ (like) them.

3 » Choose the correct option.
1 I (got)/ get up as usual at seven o'clock.
2 I talkked / talked to my mom at breakfast.
3 I checkied / checked my homework.
4 I taked / took the bus to school.
5 We played / plaid basketball after lunch.
6 I came / comed home at four o'clock.
7 I studied / studyed for a history test.
8 Then something strange happened / happenned.
9 Everything stoped / stopped.
10 I travels / traveled back in time to the year 2000.

4 a » Complete the poem with the simple past form of the verbs in parentheses.

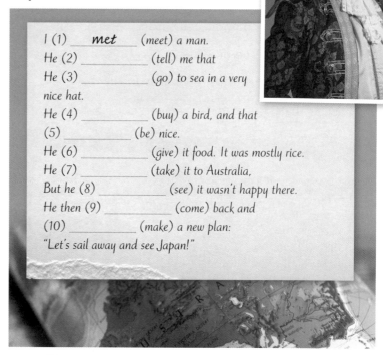

I (1) _met_ (meet) a man.
He (2) _____ (tell) me that
He (3) _____ (go) to sea in a very nice hat.
He (4) _____ (buy) a bird, and that
(5) _____ (be) nice.
He (6) _____ (give) it food. It was mostly rice.
He (7) _____ (take) it to Australia,
But he (8) _____ (see) it wasn't happy there.
He then (9) _____ (come) back and
(10) _____ (make) a new plan:
"Let's sail away and see Japan!"

b ▶47 Listen and check.

5 >>> Complete the conversation below with the correct form of the verbs in the box.

| buy | die | give | go | know | see | tell | visit |

Vicki: We (1) _went_ to a tree farm last week. We (2) _____ a new banana plant for my grandfather.
Jan: Why?
Vicki: The banana plant in his yard (3) _____. He (4) _____ us he wanted a new one. I (5) _____ it yesterday when I (6) _____ him. It's so small! But banana plants grow very fast.
Jan: I never (7) _____ that!
Vicki: The man at the tree farm (8) _____ us a lot of good information about banana plants.

98

SPEAKING

Ask how people are

1 a Complete the *Phrasebook* with the words in the box.

all right   bad   going   ~~things~~   too   you

b ▶48 Now listen and check.

PHRASEBOOK
Ask how people are
How are you?
How are (1) *things*?
How's it (2) _____?
And (3) _____?
Say how you are
Good.
Not too (4) _____.
I'm fine (thanks).
I'm (5) _____ (thank you).
Not (6) _____ good.

2 ▶49 Listen to three conversations. Check (✓) who feels good.
1 Rufus ✓
2 Ozzie ☐
3 Mr. King ☐
4 Ricardo ☐
5 Tania ☐
6 Laura ☐

3 ▶50 Listen to four more conversations. Write *F* when the people speaking are friends and *NF* when they're not friends.
1 Conversation 1   *NF*
2 Conversation 2   _____
3 Conversation 3   _____
4 Conversation 4   _____

4 ▶51 Listen and repeat the sentences. Pay special attention to stress and intonation.

Conversation 1

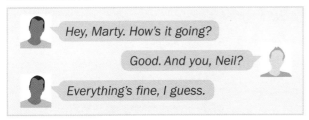

Hey, Marty. How's it going?
Good. And you, Neil?
Everything's fine, I guess.

Conversation 2

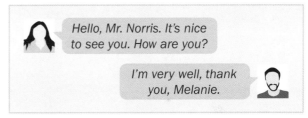

Hello, Mr. Norris. It's nice to see you. How are you?
I'm very well, thank you, Melanie.

Conversation 3

Matt

Ryan

Hi, Ryan. How are things?
Not too bad. I got an A in science!
Wow! That's great!
Thanks, Matt. How are you?
Not too good.
Really? Why's that?
I got an F on the same test …

5 Write a conversation between you and one of your friends. Ask how they are.

A: Hi! How _____?
B: I'm ☺ _____. And _____?
A: ☹ _____.
B: Why _____?
A: Because _____.

WRITING

>>> **Write a postcard**

1 Choose the correct spelling.

REMEMBER HOW TO …

check your spelling

- Check for double letters:
  (1) **arrive** / arive
  (2) sumer / **summer**
- Check verbs:
  (3) tried / tryed
  (4) enjoied / enjoyed
- Check words with the same pronunciation:
  (5) It's over there / their .
  (6) It's / Its my bike.

2 Choose the correct option.

1 I can **hear** / here the ocean.
2 We went they're / there yesterday.
3 Its / It's very near the hotel.
4 Look! There's a little / litle island.
5 It's up the street on the right / write.
6 I'm writeing / writing a postcard to my friend.

3 Underline and correct the spelling mistakes in the postcard. There are 14 mistakes to find.

1	happier	8	
2		9	
3		10	
4		11	
5		12	
6		13	
7		14	

4 Choose the correct options.

Hi Joni. I'm <u>happyer</u> than I was last year. Hour new house is beter than the old won. The yard's biger, and the too dogs love it. My knew school's near my house. I'm siting hear bye the pool at the hotel. We arriveed yesterday. Hope your OK. Have a good vaccation and right soon.
Mitchell

Hi Elizabeth!
Hello from the (1) **city** / citty of San José. I'm on vacation (2) hear / here in Costa Rica's capital. It's fun! I'm so (3) hapy / happy – this is my first time in Costa Rica.
The weather is fantastic! (4) It's / Its (5) suny / sunny all the time. My hotel's (6) realy / really cool (7) to / too . (8) It's / Its (9) swimming / swiming pool is big, and there's a great restaurant. You (10) no / know my friends Susie and Molly? (11) There / They're also here.
Yesterday we went to the Natural History Museum. I loved (12) its / it's dinosaur exhibit (a show about dinosaurs). Then we went (13) shopping / shoping. What a great day!
Miss you ☹
Sarah x

8

5 You're going to write a postcard. Make notes. Use the *Writing plan* to help you.

WRITING PLAN

1 Where are you on vacation? Is it in a city, in the mountains, or by a beach? Is it in your country or another one? ☐

_____
_____
_____

2 What do you usually do every day? What did you do yesterday? ☐

_____
_____
_____

3 What's the place like? What's the weather like? ☐

_____
_____
_____

WRITE AND CHECK

6 Write your message. Write about 50 words. Then check (✓) the stages in the *Writing plan*.

▶▶▶ Be careful with money

1 Complete the **REFLECTION POINT** with the words in the box.

careful   check   ~~important~~   much   need

2 Match the options (a–e) to the words/phrases (1–5) to make tips.

1 Decide — e — a money you have.
2 Look at how much ___ b your change when you pay.
3 Do the math. ___ c Choose again.
4 Not enough money? ___ d How much do you need?
5 Check ___ e what you want.

REFLECTION POINT

It's (1) *important* to be
(2) _____ with money.
Know how (3) _____
you have and how much you
(4) _____. And always
(5) _____ your change.

3 ▶52 Listen to the conversations. Why are the people NOT careful with money? Choose the correct option, a or b.

1 Jude doesn't …
   a check his change.
   b know how much money he has.
2 Anna doesn't …
   a think about how much she can eat.
   b want to spend too much money.
3 Peter doesn't …
   a do the math.
   b choose again.
4 William doesn't …
   a decide what he wants.
   b check his change.

SCHOOL SKILLS

101

VOCABULARY REVIEW

UNITS 1-8

1 Choose the correct options from the box below.

The weather's really (1) _____ here right now. It's windy and raining,
and we can't leave our (2) _____ . I wanted to go to the movies,
but the streets are like (3) _____ , and our yard's like a swimming
(4) _____ . You need a boat, not a (5) _____ , to go places! You can't
(6) _____ the street outside our house. The weather isn't (7) _____
for this time of the year. It's a big (8) _____ .

1	a	expensive	(b)	terrible	c	smart
2	a	house	b	capital	c	view
3	a	mountains	b	rivers	c	scenes
4	a	pool	b	ocean	c	balcony
5	a	chair	b	tent	c	car
6	a	cross	b	ride	c	drive
7	a	noisy	b	old	c	normal
8	a	box	b	problem	c	survey

2 Match the parts of the body (a–f) to the verbs (1–6).

1 eat _d_   4 touch _____
2 listen _____   5 run _____
3 look _____   6 think _____

3 Complete the paragraph with the words in the box.

break   jeans   sneakers   similar   skirt   sweatshirt   ~~wear~~

At my school we can (1) _____wear_____ what we like. I usually wear (2) _____ on my feet because
I play basketball at lunch (3) _____ . I always wear a T-shirt, and if it's a cold day, I put on
a (4) _____ or a jacket. I often wear blue (5) _____ . Most girls wear (6) _____
clothes. Not many girls wear dresses or (7) _____ s anymore.

4 Complete the words. Use the clues to help you.

1 d r i v e somewhere in a car.
2 c _____ t with your friends online or in person.
3 e _____ food at dinner time.
4 r _____ e a horse or a bike.
5 s _____ m in the pool or in the ocean.
6 d _____ e to music at a party.
7 s _____ d up to get off a chair.
8 m _____ e something to show what it is without words, using your body.

5 Match 1–3 to the similar words (a–c).

1 eat _c_   a sit
2 stand _____   b drive
3 ride _____   c drink

ALL ABOUT ME

1 What clothes do you like to wear? What are you wearing now?

2 What's your favorite food? How often do you eat it?

3 What's your dream job? Why?

102

GRAMMAR REVIEW

UNITS 1-8

1 a Choose the correct option.

1 *You do* / *Do you* live here?
2 *Is he* / *He is* OK?
3 *Can you* / *You can* remember your home phone number?
4 *Do you walk* / *walk you* to school?
5 *Do you like* / *You like* Chinese food?
6 Can they *cooking* / *cook* ?

b Complete the short answers to the questions in Exercise 1a.

1 Yes, ___*I do*___ .
2 No, _____ .
3 Yes, _____ .
4 No, _____ .
5 Yes, _____ .
6 No, _____ .

2 Choose the correct options from the box below.

We usually (1) _____ to our grandparents on the phone every week, but (2) _____ phone isn't working now. I (3) _____ know why it isn't working. They're (4) _____ in South America – I think they're in Chile now. Maybe they (5) _____ the phone or there's no signal. My mom (6) _____ them a message at the hotel, and I hope they contact (7) _____ soon.

1 a	talking	**b**	talk	c	to talk
2 a	they	b	their	c	theirs
3 a	not	b	don't	c	no
4 a	travel	b	traveled	c	traveling
5 a	is losing	b	loses	c	lost
6 a	left	b	leaving	c	leaves
7 a	ours	b	our	c	us

3 Complete the sentences with *a*, *the*, *some*, or *any*. Some sentences have more than one correct answer.

I like (1) ___*a*___ nice cup of hot chocolate in (2) _____ morning. I always take (3) _____ bottle of water with me all day. I have (4) _____ glass of orange juice with my lunch. In the afternoon I have (5) _____ tea. I don't put (6) _____ sugar or milk in my tea.

4 Complete the text with the correct form of the words in parentheses.

I (1) ___*have*___ (have) one cousin. His name (2) _____ (be) Roberto, and he's three years younger than I am. He (3) _____ (live) in Mexico now, and I'm in the USA. I (4) _____ (not see) him very often, but that's OK. I usually (5) _____ (call) him on Sundays. Roberto (6) _____ (be) always happy when I talk to him over the internet. We spent a lot of time together when we (7) _____ (be) younger, and we (8) _____ (have) fun. He's really funny and tells great jokes. There (9) _____ (not be) many people you can (10) _____ (call) "true friends," but Roberto is a true friend.

When we were young

103